About the author

Janet Impey studied fashion and dress design at Portsmouth College of Art and has worked as fashion and beauty editor on various magazines, becoming the Fashion Editor of *Woman and Home* in 1975. She is now a freelance fashion stylist and beauty writer for numerous magazines including *TV Times*, *Weight Watchers*, *Over 21*, *Woman's Own*, *Living*, *Good Housekeeping* and *Annabel*.

A WI HELP YOURSELF GUIDE

Style Made Simple

FASHION AND BEAUTY KNOW-HOW

JANET IMPEY

CENTURY

LONDON · MELBOURNE · AUCKLAND · JOHANNESBURG

Copyright © Janet Impey 1988

First published in 1988 by Century Hutchinson Ltd
Brookmount House, 62–65 Chandos Place, London WC2N 4NW

Century Hutchinson Australia (Pty) Ltd
PO Box 496, 16–22 Church Street, Hawthorn,
Victoria 3122, Australia

Century Hutchinson New Zealand Ltd
PO Box 40–086, 32–34 View Road, Glenfield,
Auckland 10, New Zealand

Century Hutchinson South Africa (Pty) Ltd
PO Box 337, Bergvlei 2012, South Africa

Photoset in 9pt Sabon (Linotron 202)
by Deltatype Ltd, Ellesmere Port, Cheshire

Printed and bound in Great Britain by
Mackays of Chatham

British Library Cataloguing in Publication Data

Impey, Janet
  Style made simple : fashion & beauty know-how
  — (A WI help-yourself guide).
  1. Beauty, Personal
  I. Title   II. Series
  646.7′2′088042   RA778

ISBN 0–7126–1976–3

CONTENTS

Introduction

INTRODUCTION

Have you ever stood in front of your overflowing wardrobe and decided you have nothing to wear? Have you ever looked in the mirror and been unhappy with your appearance? If so, join the club. We all have days when nothing seems to work, just as there are days when everything seems to fall into place. Then, you will not only look good, but feel good too. Confidence is the bonus that comes from getting it right and in its turn it acts as the inspiration for individual flair. Identifying the recipe for this success is what this book is all about, for to achieve a top-to-toe sense of style should not be a chance occurrence but an effortless, everyday pleasure.

In my capacity as a beauty writer and fashion stylist I have met women of all ages, shapes and sizes and listened to their concerns over their particular appearance problems. I see their fashion and beauty potential, but they only see their faults. The desire to do ourselves down seems to be inherent, and whether we are obsessed with crooked teeth, a fat waistline or a big nose, most of us seem oblivious to our assets. Removing the blinkers, looking beyond the faults and thinking positively about the plus points is an essential step towards having a sense of our own worth.

Simply emphasizing your best features isn't enough however, since creating an overall good impression depends on everything balancing and harmonizing, inside and outside your body. Your general wellbeing is reflected in your appearance and thus a sensible diet and exercise routine has an essential part to play and knows no age barrier. Combine health and fitness with commonsense dressing and you have some of the magic ingredients for looking good. But there's more. Your make-up may be perfect but does your hairstyle suit your face? Do the colours of your clothes detract from your total appearance or do they seem to make your face look brighter? Above all, do you feel comfortable in the style you have chosen? By simply explaining how all these aspects link together I hope to show how easy it is to develop a style which will suit you and the way you live. Start by buying a full-length mirror. It will open your eyes to a whole new image!

ALL ABOUT OUR FIGURE

Understanding your body size, its shape and proportions, is the only way in which you will learn to dress well. Once you have assessed your figure type, you can then apply as many tricks of the trade as you deem necessary to improve your own body image. Using clothes to flatter your shape is merely an attempt to create an illusion of a perfect figure and to disguise your own flaws. There's nothing wrong with that, so long as you can come to terms with, and even be happy with, your own body. Keeping it healthy, toned-up and trim is more important, for instance, than whether or not you have broad shoulders. Although you may be able to disguise the latter you cannot alter your basic structure, so accepting that broad shoulders are an asset, instead of a fault, is the first step towards feeling at ease within yourself.

It's not really surprising that we have trouble loving our own looks. Early attitudes to appearance learned from childhood suggest that too much study of form in the mirror is considered vain and looked on as unhealthy self-interest. Unlike her Continental counterpart, who constantly praises her children's good looks and positively encourages them to take an interest in their appearance from a very young age, the British mum instils no sense of value in this way of thinking. Consequently, from generation to generation, most women in this country have trouble accepting compliments, see only their faults when looking in the mirror and generally have difficulty projecting their identity.

Dissatisfaction with appearance invariably leads to wanting the opposite to what you have – witness the blonde who wants to be brunette, the tall person who wants to be petite, the curvaceous woman who yearns to be boyishly built. Everyone has an ideal figure in mind when they see themselves in the mirror, and yet everyone's idea of a standard is vastly different. The truth is that although you may not conform to your own vision of beauty, every woman can look attractive and appealing when she dresses to flatter her own individual looks.

First, you need some honest scrutiny and the answers to several questions. Take a good look at yourself in a full-length mirror. As you are limited by your frame and by how you compare to the rough average of what dress designers call the 'norm', it's important to make a note of a few measurements. However, each manufacturer interprets the statistics differently, which is why some labels will fit you better than others and why it is always worth being open-minded and trying on clothes in several sizes until you establish a few favourite manufacturers who suit your particular needs. There are also specialist companies catering for the big, small and tall although there are very few other alternatives in sizing. The reason is simply because the huge variety of styles for women makes it impossible for stores to stock wide size ranges of each item. As a general rule of thumb, however, I've found that the more expensive the item of clothing the more generous the cut and the cheaper the garment the skimpier the sizing is likely to be.

Standard Clothes Size Chart (in centimetres)

British Size	8	10	12	14	16	18
American Size	6	8	10	12	14	16
European Size	36	38	40	42	44	46
Height	158	160	162	164	166	168
Shoulder width	11.5–11.6	11.7–11.8	11.9–12	12.1–12.2	12.3–12.4	12.5–12.6
Shoulder/knee	94	95.5	97	98.5	100	101.5
Neck/waist	39	39.5	40	40.5	41	41.5
Upper arm	23.2–24	24.6–25.4	26–26.8	27.4–28.2	28.8–29.9	30.2–31
Wrist	13.8–14.2	14.4–14.8	15–15.4	15.6–16	16.2–16.6	16.9–17.2
Outer arm	70.7–71	71.7–72	72.7–73	73.7–74	74.7–75	75.7–76
Under arm	41.4–41.6	41.6–41.8	41.8–42	42–42.2	42.2–42.4	42.4–42.6
Bust	78–80	82–84	86–88	90–92	94–96	98–100
Waist	57–59	61–63	65–67	69–71	73–75	77–79
Hips	84–86	88–90	92–94	96–98	100–102	104–106
Thigh	51–52	53–54	55–56	57–58	59–60	61–62
Knee	32.5–33	33.5–34	34.5–35	35.5–36	36.5–37	37.5–38
Ankle	29.5–30	30.5–31	31.5–32	32.5–33	33.5–34	34.5–35

Measuring Your Height

Your height will indicate whether you are small, average or tall. Small is 5 ft 3 inches (160cm) and under, average usually means 5 ft 4 inches to 5 ft 7 inches (162.5cm to 170cm) and tall is 5 ft 8 inches (173cm) and over.

Measuring Your Body

Next, using the diagram as a guide, measure your body and get to know where it differs from the 'standard' chart which gives some of the guidelines that manufacturers use when making clothes. Measure shoulder width, shoulder to knee length, nape of neck to waist, upper arm, wrist, outer arm and under arm sleeve length, bust, waist, hips, thigh, knee and ankle. Compare these to the chart to ascertain your most likely clothes size and to note where you're out of line with the standard sizing.

Whatever your size, there is an ideal set of body proportions. Don't expect to be perfect, but if you know you are seriously out of proportion it will help you to choose clothes that will minimize the discrepancy.

Estimating Proportion

Standing straight with feet flat on the floor and arms by your sides, check to see if:

- your crutch is approximately at the halfway point
- your waist comes halfway between crutch and armpit
- your elbows come halfway down the arm and line up with the waist
- your third knuckle comes at crutch height
- your knees are halfway down the leg
- your nipples are 3 inches (7.6cm) below your armpits
- your shoulders are 1 inch (2.5cm) wider than your hips

Body Shapes

Coupled with the fact that you may be small, average or tall in height, you can also decide how your contours match up to the three basic physiological shapes – ectomorph (small framed and slim); mesomorph (medium build and fairly well proportioned); endomorph (heavy build, plump and curvy). Some people will fit into these categories exactly, but others, while belonging predominantely to one group, are mixtures. The classic pear-shape, for instance, regarded as a peculiarly British affliction, can be common to all figure types, and yet is one of the easier faults to disguise. There are some general

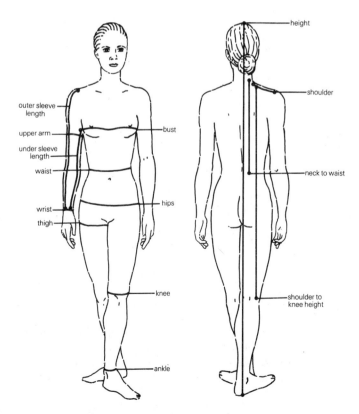

guidelines to follow when dressing for your particular figure type and I have also included a section of suggestions for specific areas which may be a problem for you. Much of it is just sheer commonsense and you'll probably find that you have instinctively been doing the right thing all along! On the other hand, it may give you pleasure to flout the rules or tailor them to suit your own personality (more of that later). Personally, I'm all for breaking the rules, but suggest that before you disregard the advice you make sure you have a thorough understanding of the basic principles involved.

Small
Petite women have small bone structure and can be perfectly proportioned for their height, boyishly slim or on the plump side. The essential rule is to wear everything scaled to your size, regardless of your weight, or you'll risk being overwhelmed by your clothing.

Do ...

● Keep your outfits simple and unfussy. This doesn't mean you can't enjoy a soft, feminine style if that suits you, but use fabric to suggest femininity rather than silhouette and keep details like a lace collar, for instance, neat rather than flouncy.

● Do pay special attention to shoulders, neckline, sleeve length and skirt length. Good fit is really important for small women.

● Do scale down to your size details such as pockets, collars and prints. Generally, neat styles look best on small bodies.

● Tone colours. A one-colour scheme outfit will give the illusion of height, especially if you also tone in tights and shoes.

● Concentrate on vertical lines in your clothes and this will give the impression of elongating your size. Boyish figures can get away with ribbed tube knits.

● Keep belts self-toning rather than contrasting since the latter will only break up the body line.

● Stretch the body visually by using long, thin scarves, long necklaces, narrow lapels on jackets and heeled shoes.

Don't .

● Wear bulky layers, shapes like tent dresses or mohair coats.

● Indulge in exaggerated details such as patch pockets, epaulettes, wide lapels, full skirts and wide trousers.

● Indulge in large splashy prints and bold plaids. These are taboo for you.

● Wear wide horizontal stripes or contrast coloured tops and bottoms. It will make you look little and round.
● Carry large shoulder bags, wear chunky jewellery or other very bold accessories. They will look out of proportion.

Average
Don't knock the word, it can give you great freedom when choosing your clothes and a chance to experiment with fashion, especially if you are slim and have a flamboyant character. If you are on the plump side, you may prefer a more conservative approach, since classic lines are generally more flattering. Make sure you keep accessories in proportion to your frame.

Tall
Model slim, yours is the ideal figure to wear anything from jeans to designer dresses with great panache. Take advantage of your height by wearing innovative silhouettes and bold accessories. If you are statuesque, your generous proportions give you a sensuous appeal and you can emphasize this by wearing perfectly tailored, but soft, clothes which will accentuate the curves.

Do . . .
● Make use of dramatic accessories such as large hats, chunky jewellery, eye-catching bags.
● Invest in sweeping silhouettes like capes, full, flared coats and bias-cut or full skirts.
● Add extra fullness with longer length tiered skirts, ruffles and flounces if you are slim.
● Wear bold geometric and big, splashy prints, plaids and bold stripes. Border prints will look good in moderation provided you have a bold personality to match.
● Hide extra pounds with tunic tops, three-quarter jackets or suits with longer jackets and straighter skirts.
● Check that sleeves and hems are long enough for your proportions and lengthen them if necessary.

Don't .
● Wear small prints, frilly designs, empire lines, puffed sleeves or anything which smacks of 'little-girl' looks.
● Wear suits with very short jackets and very short skirts.
● Wear extremely high heels – shoes with a moderate heel are better.
● Wear dainty jewellery or use small accessories.

Figure Faults   To create a balanced body shape, learn to enhance your best features and draw attention away from what you consider your worst figure traits. You can use line and the cut of clothes to give the impression you wish by creating an illusion or focusing on a particular point. Once you understand the *trompe d'oeil* tricks you can make almost any fashion work for your body shape.

Short Neck

Do . . .
- Wear V necklines, scoop necks, U-necklines or camisole tops – in fact, anything that elongates your natural neckline.
- Always leave the top few buttons of a shirt collar unbuttoned.
- Use long necklaces but small earrings.
- Choose a short, soft hairstyle which bares the neckline but has some fullness at top and sides. Wear long hair swept up into a soft knot or twist.

Don't .
- Wear high collars, crew-neck sweaters, polo necks, jackets with mandarin collars or any style which focuses on the neck.
- Choose blouses with pussycat bows or Victorian pie-crust collars.
- Wear scarves tied at the neck or cravats.
- Wear chokers, short necklaces, multi-strand necklaces, dangling or chunky earrings.
- Choose a hairstyle which has volume at neck level or a very short, severe cut which emphasizes the neck.

Narrow or Sloping Shoulders

Do . . .
- Wear tops that create width to balance the hips, especially tops with an extended shoulderline, cap sleeves, set in sleeves with padded shoulders and puff or pleated sleeve-heads.
- Choose necklines with horizontal lines, such as boat necks, wide scoops, wide round collars, epaulettes, small round yokes with gathering from the yoke, shoulder ruffles.
- Wear a combination of a light-coloured top with width at the shoulders teamed with a darker slimline skirt or narrow-leg trousers.

Don't .
- Wear body-hugging tops such as rib sweaters which emphasize your problem.
- Choose styles with raglan, kimono or dolman sleeves or loose, roomy overblouses which droop at the shoulderline.
- Wear big bows, scarves or chunky jewellery at the neck

V-necklines for short necks

Wide shoulders for narrow or sloping shoulders

Chanel-style jackets for a big bust

nor anything which shortens the width from shoulder to shoulder.

● Wear very full skirts or wide trousers which might emphasize a pear-shaped appearance.

Large Bust

Do . . .

● Invest in a good bra and get expert help and fitting service from a trained lingerie specialist.

● Wear tops that are classically simple and don't cling.

● Choose V necklines, open collars and cowl necks.

● Choose styles with tailored, set-in, narrow sleeves.

● Wear figure-skimming cardigan jackets or jackets with neat, vertical lines like the Chanel style.

● Enjoy wearing eye-catching bottom halves such as floral skirts or trousers with interesting styling details to take the eye away from a big bust.

Don't .

● Wear any tight-fitting tops, clingy sweaters, or sheer-fabric blouses.

● Choose blouse styles with ruffles, tucks, puffed sleeves, smock fronts or large patch pockets.

● Add to your horizontal lines by choosing boat or slit necklines. Wear wide belts, wrap belts or tight belts.

● Wear splashy prints, bold checks or stripes or any pattern that will draw attention to the bust area.

Flat Chest

Do . . .

● Wear easy-fitting blouses which add fullness. Choose soft fabrics that drape well and look for ruffled fronts, tie necklines, bow collars, pin-tucked fronts, puffed or cap sleeves.

13

● Wear jackets with padded shoulders and wide lapels.
● Wear big bloused shirtwaister style dresses belted at the waist, empire line and smock dresses.
● Choose bulky, textured sweaters. Mohair is a must.
● Go for a layered look with waistcoats, cardigans and jackets.
● Make the most of horizontal stripes to give your figure some curves.

Don't .
● Wear tight-fitting tops or sweaters.
● Choose camisole tops, crew-neck sweaters or round-collared blouses.
● Wear very full skirts, wide trousers or single-breasted jackets with narrow lapels.

Heavy Upper Arms

Do . . .
● Wear sleeves which are loose fitting and don't hug the upper arm. Dolman and kimono sleeves are good, as are short, wide sleeves with deep armholes.
● Wear blouses with elbow-length puffed sleeves.
● Wear either loose-fitting jackets over tops or shawls which drape and blur the outline of the arm.
● Draw attention away from upper arms by wearing an unusual wrist watch or bracelet.

Don't .
● Wear very tight sweaters or any style with clingy sleeves.
● Wear strapless, sleeveless or halter tops that bare the arms.

Short Waist

Do . . .
● Choose trousers and skirts with narrow waistbands or with no waistbands at all.
● Wear skirts styled with yokes or basques so that the eye is drawn downwards.
● Wear lean jackets and tunics, longline sweaters and waistcoats which elongate the upper body.
● Wear dresses with dropped waists, straight body-skimming styles or unbelted silhouettes.

Don't .
● Wear any high-waisted styles or skirts and trousers with wide waistbands.
● Choose wide belts, wrap belts or any belt which emphasizes your waist and makes your torso appear even shorter.

   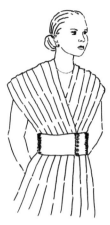

...ide lapels for a ...nall bust	Heavy upperarms need deep-cut armholes and wide sleeve	Basque style skirts elongate a short waist	Wide belts counter a long waist

Long Waist

Do . . . ● Choose trousers and skirts with wide waistbands and wear wide belts and cummerbunds.
● Wear cropped or bolero jackets and waistcoats with below-knee skirts or tailored trousers.

Don't . ● Choose vertically-striped blouses and tops, tunic lines, unbelted lines, or drop-waisted styles.
● Wear short, over-the-knee skirts, cropped pants or low-waisted jeans.

Thick Waist

Do . . . ● Wear body-skimming tunic styles, overblouses and smocks, loose-fitting waistcoats, longline jackets, drop-waisted dresses, skirts with basques and gentle gathers.
● Wear padded shoulders, V necklines and shoulder and neckline detail on blouses and dresses to focus attention away from the waist.

Don't . . . ● Wear figure-hugging silhouettes or belted dresses.
● Wear tailored blouses or sweaters tucked into a waist-band.
● Wear skirts or trousers that are gathered at the waist.
● Wear wide or wrap belts.

Big Hips

Do . . .
- Wear A-line skirts, wrap skirts, gored skirts, panelled skirts, skirts that hug from waist to top of hip and then flare gently.
- Choose fabrics that don't add bulk, for example wool crêpe or wool gabardine.
- Choose classic, straight-leg trousers but, on the whole, skirts are more flattering.
- Choose longline sweaters and jackets which don't end at your widest point. Try a cropped jacket and a bias-cut skirt for a change.
- Use jewellery and scarves to focus attention upwards.

Don't .
- Buy loud-patterned or brightly-coloured trousers or skirts.
- Choose skirts and trousers in heavy fabrics such as corduroy, angora, mohair, bouclé wool or clingy jersey.
- Wear culottes, divided skirts, pleated or gathered skirts.
- Carry an oversized bag at hip level.

Fat Bottom

Do . . .
- Wear softly gathered shirtwaister dresses, smock and caftan styles, A-line and gored skirts and skirts with some fullness.
- Wear straight-leg trousers, although skirts will be more flattering.
- Wear suits with longline jackets, elongated sweaters, overblouses and tunic tops.
- Wear padded shoulders, pleated sleeveheads, epaulettes and extended sleeves to balance the lower half of the body.
- Wear vertical and diagonal stripes.

Don't .
- Wear clingy knits, dresses, skirts or trousers.
- Wear tapered skirt lines or trousers that narrow at the hems.
- Wear cropped pants, shorts, cropped knitwear or short jackets.

Big Legs

Do . . .
- Wear pleated or roomy straight-leg trousers.
- Wear dresses or skirts with soft gathering, pleats or mid-calf-length flared skirts.
- Wear sheer tights in neutral colours, matching your hosiery to your shoes.
- Choose plain, comfortable shoes in styles that don't date, such as classic courts and pumps with medium heels.

Don't .
- Wear very light, textured or opaque tights.
- Choose T-strap or ankle-strap shoes, flat sandals, or short, mid-calf or light-coloured boots.
- Wear short or narrow skirts, shorts or any style which makes a feature of the legs.

Short Legs

Do . . .
- Wear slim skirts to the knee or just below or mid-calf skirts with high-heel boots.
- Wear narrow, straight-leg trousers with medium to high heeled shoes and cropped jackets and knitwear.
- Wear a head-to-toe colour scheme to elongate yourself and use accessories to focus attention on the top half.
- Always choose a swimsuit with high-cut legs.

Don't .
- Wear mini skirts, culottes or any style which makes a focal point of the legs.
- Wear fancy patterned tights or trousers tucked into boots.
- Wear short boots, mid-calf boots or flat shoes.
- Wear tunics, hip-length sweaters and jackets, tiered, drop-waisted or border pattern skirts, trousers and skirts with a horizontal pattern.

Tips

- Let me explode the myth that black is slimming! Black, or any other dark colour, actually silhouettes the body against almost any background and thus makes a person who is big look even more so. A large woman is better off in soft colours that draw attention to the face not the frock.

- Vertical stripes are slimming but a single vertical stripe is more effective than a mass. When lines are repeated the eye actually moves sideways from line to line as well as up and down, so the overall message is diffused.

- Horizontal stripes can be used across the body to suggest curves but beware of using them on anything other than an attractive part of the body.

- Invest in some really stylish accessories – a beautiful belt if you have a trim waist to show off, a stunning brooch if you want to emphasize your neckline.

- If your clothes are too tight, or look strained, it only emphasizes the very part of your body that you are trying to disguise. Go up a size. Nobody sees the label but you!

Wear slim skirts and
short jackets in one
colour for short legs

Softly-gathered mid-calf skirts
suit large legs

Tunic styles disguise a
thick waist

2

DRESSING

TO SUIT

YOUR

PERSONALITY

Wearing clothes that make you instinctively feel good is allowing your personality to influence your choice. What makes one person love a sharp geometric print while another might prefer a floral pattern? It's simply the outward expression of your inner characteristics. Identifying and accentuating your clothing personality is the key to your wardrobe planning. Good and bad buys are easily divided into clothes which are either often worn or seldom worn.

Take a good look at your favourite outfits – the ones you always rely on when you have important fixtures and those in which you feel most at ease. Ignore the colours for the moment and just look at the styles and fabrics. Are they tailored, with geometric lines and sharp angles, and made from stiff or shiny fabrics? Do they have big blocks of contrast colour, wide stripes, Aztec prints or square patterns? Or do you prefer soft lines like cowl necks, raglan sleeves, curved lapels, prints with rounded shapes such as scrolls and florals, fabrics which fold and drape, textured material such as angora, soft tweeds and velvets?

The clue, apart from your favourite clothes, is your body shape. If you are tall and angular you are more likely to enjoy the rather dramatic shapes of the first group, while a curved body looks better in the more romantic, softer styles of the second. In between the two extremes are the conventional classic and the sporty, casual types. See if you can recognize yourself from the following descriptions of a 'fashion type'. Even if you overlap from one group to another (and there are plenty of variations within each category), knowing the general direction in which your instincts lie will help you to pinpoint why certain clothes look better on you than others.

Dramatic A tall, slender or large-boned frame with bony, angular features and often dark, exotic colouring; those are the outward signs of the dramatic dresser while her character can be quite formidable. She can be reserved, assertive, strong-willed, quick-tempered, artistic, decisive, sophisticated, organized, punctual, tidy and have a strong sense of duty and responsibility. If you are not tall but have dramatic features you will only be able to add dramatic touches to your clothes. Otherwise, dramatics look good in extremes of fashion, from ultra-sharp straight lines in severe, plain fabrics to incredibly billowy clothes. Vivid colours and bold prints, metallic weaves, lavish trims, elaborate jewellery and all the rather theatrical styles (this applies to hair and make-up, too) are all dramatic qualities which will enhance your looks. However, if you are tall, angular and fair, your softer colouring will look better with a more muted, sophisticated look.

Ideas for dramatic dressing

Dramatic Pointers

- Choose overscaled patterns in geometric designs, stripes, squares, Aztecs, large spots, stylized designs.
- Choose styles with sharp angles, wide shoulder pads, wide lapels, overstated detail.
- Choose high contrast in large areas of block colour.
- Choose smooth, shiny or stiff fabrics such as wool gabardine, cotton drill, PVC, taffeta.
- Choose extreme lengths – overshort or overlong.
- Wear bold jewellery, wide belts, large earrings, patent shoes.
- Wear hats – turbans, wide brims – anything dramatic!

Classic The typical classic type is a scaled-down dramatic, avoiding the extremes of style but concentrating on quality fabrics, soft straight lines, conventional tailoring and immaculate grooming. Classics usually have a well-proportioned body, medium colouring, even, regular facial features and an ordered approach to life. Although everyone can wear classic clothes, the true classic has a sense of formality and poise which suits her personality and is echoed in her choice of clothes. A woman with dramatic qualities will just look boring in classic clothes, whereas a romantic type will feel uncomfortable in the restrictive severity of the styles. By the very nature of classic clothes it would be easy to become too 'medium' and matronly, so a classic woman must always be seen crisply turned out, beautifully made-up and with a controlled hairstyle which always looks neat. When classics look untidy or cluttered with the wrong clothes they look disastrous, especially if they are small-boned and inclined to look gamine. Inexpensive clothes really do look cheap on the classics, so clothes of quality, not quantity, will be the cornerstone of your wardrobe.

Classic Pointers

Classic chic

- Choose medium weight, shiny or matt fabrics with a smooth finish.
- Choose natural fibres – fine cottons and jerseys, wool crêpe, flannel and fine knits.
- Choose medium- to small-scale prints such as evenly-spaced stripes, spots, checks and paisley.
- Wear classic designs with good tailoring and modest proportions.
- Wear clean-cut lines: straight, tailored, or soft-pleat skirts; neat necklines; dresses with straight lines or soft draping and folds and set-in sleeves rather than raglan.
- Wear real jewellery, antique or modern, good leather belts and shoes, silk scarves, well constructed handbags and neat hats.

Natural　Sporty, casual looks with soft, unstructured lines in beautiful textures are the hallmarks of a natural. From tall and sturdy to small and boyish, the natural woman has plenty of energy and a friendly, informal manner. Sportswear always looks good on her, even if she is not an athletic build. Suedes and leathers, handwoven fabrics, textured tweeds, bouclé wools, ethnic prints, tartans, checks and paisleys are the natural choice of fabrics, though for more formal occasions avoid shiny fabrics and go for plain-coloured matt fabric – heavy crêpe, raw silk or jersey. Petite naturals need to enhance their neat, perky character and scale everything down by wearing lighter-weight fabrics which won't overwhelm their youthful quality. Too much make-up or an over-elaborate hairstyle, even too much jewellery, will look incongruous on a natural, although she is the only type that can get away with jeans and a T-shirt at a dinner party and still look stunning.

The classic casual look

● Choose sporty, easy styles using textured fabrics to create softness. Wear denim, flannel, cord, tweeds, linen, brushed cotton, raw silk, chunky knits, leather and suede.

● Choose ethnic jewellery made from metals, wood, bone, rafia, leather and all natural materials.

● Choose styles which are unfussy and unstructured and which have open necklines.

● Choose soft patterns on stiffer fabrics and linear patterns on softer ones. Herringbones, scrolls, paisley, stripes, spots, florals, jungle prints, checks and tartans all look good.

● Wear the minimum amount of make-up and keep hairstyles in a windblown, casual cut.

● Choose shoes and boots with medium to flat heels and a satchel or soft pouch style of bag.

Romantic

A full-blown romantic seeks femininity in both style and fabric. Often curvy in build, the roundness of the romantic shape is enhanced by soft drapes or crisply full silhouette. Fabrics should be luxurious and soft, with a sheen, and prints should be a curvy design. Evening wear looks superb on a romantic, who is in her element wearing silk, satin, chiffon, lace, brocade, velvet and other glamorous fabrics. As long as the styles are feminine she can wear exaggerated designs and sophisticated prints, strong make-up and pretty hairstyles. The romantic character is a mix of a fun-loving, sunny and outgoing nature which is affected by mood and therefore can be sulky. An air of being disorganized disguises a surprising grasp of practicalities but romantics are terrific hoarders and just love food, shoes and pretty underwear. The slim, small-boned romantic is perfect for the dainty styles and delicate fabrics which compliment her build. Fresh, youthful designs in cottons, lightweight voiles, broderie anglaise or thin jersey suit her better than shiny or glittery fabrics which are too overpowering. Romantics can also veer towards the natural, since the soft easy lines of the casual styles will suit some, and also towards the classic on

Romantic appeal

occasions, though it is essential to keep a sexy, feminine feel to these styles as otherwise the tendency is to look 'jolly hockeysticks' or frumpy.

Romantic Pointers

- Choose soft, feminine lines which emphasize body curves.
- Look for gathers, drapes, folds, bias cuts in soft luxurious materials.
- Wear skirts with drape or ease at the waist – wrap, fluted, slit or tulip shape.
- Wear jackets short, waisted, belted or peplum style. Coats should have plenty of drape.
- Choose glitzy jewellery, delicate in detail, with hearts, bows and flowers, and soft wide belts with ornate buckles.
- Wear pretty shoes with buttons and bows and soft, feminine boots.
- Wear soft necklines and a soft hairstyle with waves and curls; use pretty make-up for day and a more glamorous sparkle for evening.

Personality and Your Figure Type

The idea of categorizing yourself may not appeal to you at all, yet learning how your body shape relates to your clothes type is a step towards adapting the right styles to suit your colouring and your lifestyle. Adjusting the clothes to fit in with your own figure requirements means experimenting with styles that you may have previously rejected. Look at your wardrobe again with fresh eyes and try to use the knowledge you have gained about yourself to acquire a sense of balance between a visually pleasing silhouette and your instinctive reaction that what you are wearing feels right for your personality.

3

COLOUR

Colour is the most personal aspect of fashion and the most complex. The colour in your wardrobe reflects a myriad messages, some more obvious than others. Psychologists, for instance, maintain that wearing red (usually associated with sex and aggression) highlights our energetic, dominant streak and our desire to stand out in a crowd, while blue indicates a more reserved and tranquil mood. We may be instinctively attracted to the colours which suit us, but there are other influences at work. If, for instance, you associate navy with school uniform you may detest it, or if your husband dislikes a certain colour you will probably never feel comfortable wearing it; even if it does suit you.

By far and away the biggest influence, however, is the fashion industry itself. Seasonal trends dictate the shades, with dominant themes to which your eye soon becomes accustomed continually highlighted in the stores. Consequently, if a strong fuchsia pink constantly appears you may buy it simply because the choice is limited and the store isn't stocking the softer pink which may suit your colouring better. And therein lies the secret. Colour should not dominate to such a degree that it detracts from your face – your most important accessory! If, when you walk into a room, people notice your pink sweater instead of you as a whole, then the shade of pink is wrong for you, affects your make-up, and altogether does nothing to enhance your best features.

As a general rule of thumb, the darker you are, the better the vibrant and darker colours suit you; the fairer you are, the softer and lighter the colours should be. Within the colour spectrum, however, are clear and muted colours in both warm and cool tones. So how do you decide which looks best? Most colour analysts suggest that the colours divide naturally into four seasonal colour palettes and for a fee – well spent, in my opinion – they will interpret the range of colours which do the most for your skin tones and hair colouring. You can follow the same principles yourself by experimenting with different coloured clothes and make-up.

Colour Analysis

Your first job is to decide whether your skin has cool or warm undertones and you can do this by testing two different foundations either at home or at a cosmetics counter. Ask the assistant to help. Most foundations are based on yellow/orange or blue/red pigments and the names are often a giveaway. Try a thick streak of a warm rose and a cool beige on each cheek and leave them for a few moments. The correct base will appear to be absorbed into your skin while the wrong base will just sit on the surface and not look right. Like foundation, your skin comprises varying degrees of yellow and blue pigments, and these make up your skin undertones. Some people have very obvious skin tones and it is immediately apparent which colour group is best; others can be borderline cases, with an equal balance of yellow and blue pigmentation. This means that you will look equally good in certain shades of both cool and warm colours and will have greater flexibility in your choice of clothes.

Once you know whether your skin tones are warm or cool you can confirm this by placing colours next to your face. If the base tones harmonize with your skin they will look good, but the colours with the wrong base tone will not look so pleasing.

Place a mirror in good natural light and remove all make-up. Clip your hair away from your face and wear a plain white T-shirt. Collect together a good selection of tops and scarves of various colours and sort them into yellow-based and blue-based colours. Any colour with warmth is yellow-based, including certain shades of grey, navy and blue as well as the more obvious ones like grass greens, peach and coral, geranium red, turquoise, tan and beige. Cool colours will include the sharp brights like acid lemon, cherry red, silver grey, emerald green as well as pastel pinks and cornflower blue.

The easiest comparison is between a blue-toned rose pink and a yellow-toned apricot or peach. Hold each colour against your skin and look at your face, not the colour in question. Your skin tone will respond to the right one, which will bring a healthy colour to your face, minimize shadows and make your face stand out, pushing the colour into the background. The wrong colour will make your complexion look muddy, pale or sallow, accentuate lines or shadows around the mouth, eyes and nose, and may age your face or make it look insignificant.

If you are still undecided, there are clues to be had from the iris of your eye. If it has a distinct grey rim, you are more likely to look better in cool tones. If it has flecks of yellow mixed with your eye colour, you will probably look best in warm tones.

Apart from deciding on the amount of warmth or coolness that suits your skin, the depth of tone is important since the amount of light in a colour is reflected on to your face. If you are fair, for instance, a dark navy will appear to cut off your face, whereas a french navy with more light will be more flattering. Too much light, on the other hand, can make some faces look drained, which is why a stark white or black next to the face is often difficult for the majority of people to wear.

The third important ingredient is the clarity of tone. According to your complexion, either clear or muted colours will look best. Clear colours will look hard on the wrong complexion and zing on the right one. Muted colours will look soft and pretty on the right complexion and muddy on the wrong one.

Cool/Clear

Often described as the winter season, this category frequently includes olive-skinned, dark-eyed and raven-haired people. Although darker skin often appears golden, most blacks, orientals and olive-skinned people look stunning in clear, bright, vivid or icy colours but sallow in warm ones. A winter season skin can also be beige or very translucent white, often with no cheek colour. Hair can vary from light to charcoal brown or an attractive grey; the eyes are deep coloured, usually grey-browns, grey-blues, grey-greens or dark blue, often combined with white flecks.

Best colours   Clear vivid colours and sharp contrasts: pure white, taupe, silver grey to charcoal, black, deep navy through to bright navy, royal and electric blue, chinese blue, icy blue, royal purple, icy violet, fuchsia pink, magenta, cerise, shocking pink, icy pink, acid lemon, emerald, pine green, pillar-box red, cherry, bright burgundy, damson and all blue reds.

Cool/Muted

Often described as the summer season, light brunettes, dark ash browns and blondes generally fall into this category and suit the softer smoky colours of the cool palette. Complexions are often fair, rose-beige or pink with high colour and sometimes freckles. Eyes tend to be blue, aqua, soft hazel or grey-blue, often with a noticeable grey rim around the iris and sometimes with irregular white flecks inside it.

Best colours   Cool pastel colours and soft neutrals: soft white, pinky beige, mushroom, blue greys, rose browns, cocoa brown, denim blue, grey, navy, airforce blue, sky blue, powder blue, lavender blue, green-blue, aqua, duck-egg blue, blue pinks, pastel pink, deep rose, blue reds, raspberry, burgundy, red browns, pale primrose, plum, mauve, orchid, silver green, jade, sea green.

Warm/Clear

Typical of the spring season are golden blondes, strawberry blondes, honey brown to warm mid-browns, and carrot redheads. Eyes can be as clear as glass and are often blue, green or aqua, though golden brown or hazel eyes with a mix or brown, green and gold are also common – as is the iris with a sunburst of white/gold rays mixed with steel blue. Complexions are usually a delicate blend of peaches and cream, creamy ivory or peachy-beige and are usually finely textured with a bright, clear quality and a tendency to blush easily.

Best colours Clear warm colours that are bright and crisp: ivory, oatmeal, creamy beige, camel, tan, honey, terracotta, cinnamon, yellow grey, banana yellow, clear gold, corn, buttercup, yellow green, lime, turquoise, aquamarine, light royal blue, periwinkle blue, light navy, blue violet, hyacinth, poppy red, flame, geranium, tangerine, peach, apricot, bright coral, salmon.

Warm/Muted

The autumn season comprises striking redheads ranging from carrot to coppery auburn, brunettes with red or gold overtones, golden brown, golden grey and chestnut brown with a variety of warm skin tones – creamy, peachy, fair with freckles, sallow or pale. Most common colouring for eyes is brown or green, a mix of cloudy browns and golds, olive green and amber.

Best colours Rich warm colours that are earthy and vibrant: oyster white, earthy beiges, oatmeal, camel, tan, bronze, coffee, chocolate, chestnut, mahogany, brown-pinks, rosewood, deep apricot, salmon, strong coral, all oranges, rust, terracotta, tomato red, yellow golds, ochre, mustard, lime, moss, olive, forest green, grass green, turquoise, periwinkle blue, kingfisher, peacock blue, hyacinth.

Tips

● Within the groupings there will be one or two colours that look particularly good, while others may be borderline cases – perhaps too overwhelming or not strong enough for your particular colouring. If so, look at the corresponding colours of the other cool or warm group as the case may be and experiment with the depth and intensity of your tones.

● If your hair is coloured or highlighted the tones can be misleading, so use a white scarf to cover it up when you are studying your skin tones. If your skin is warm and your hair is cool – for instance, blonde with ash tones – it can confuse the eye, so ideally you should re-do your hair with more golden highlights in keeping with your skin tone. A real borderline case, however, can get away with wearing some cool tones next to the face.

● When you have decided on your warm or cool tones use make-up in the same range and see if the overall effect brings your face to life. Use gold metal earrings with warm tones, silver or platinum with cool tones.

● A colour that looks rich and beautiful on one person can look cheap and quite inappropriate on another and this is especially true of the cool vivid colours. Among the darker skins a small proportion will have yellow-based skin and, on them, the bright clear cool colours will leave their complexion looking faintly powdery. In this case, try the rich golds and saffrons and compare the effect.

● Young children are in touch with what suits them and know instinctively which colours they prefer. In adult life we are swamped with choice and often lose our colour direction, though we are good at putting our favourite colours in our décor or our flower arrangements. Look for clues in your surroundings.

● Use your own judgement when it comes to colour selection. If you ask the advice of a friend, she may advise you wrongly because she would like to see you in colours that she likes – and if she is the opposite colour group to yours, it's not going to work for you!

● The colours that suit you best should be worn close to your face so that they bring your best features into focus. A necklace or scarf achieves the same effect if you prefer a neutral coloured top.

Creative Colour

Once you know the group that makes the best of your colouring your clothes will be easier to coordinate, since the same base colour will give you unlimited opportunities to try out unusual combinations. Colours fall into four general categories:

The Elegant Colours
The useful neutrals permit the beauty of line and design to show through. These are the quiet beiges, the creams and whites, taupes and greys, browns, and navy through to black. These unassuming colours never date and form the backdrop for endless versatility through the addition of different accessories. For clothes that are often worn – coats, raincoats, suits – these basic colours are an obvious choice.

The Youthful Colours
Young in spirit, these colours are not necessarily confined to the young in years. Chalky pastels suggest innocence and

prettiness. A soft, harmonious blending of pink, sky blue and lemon are gentle reminders of femininity and are always easy on the eye. Red and navy are also associated with youth and Edith Head, famous costume designer to the Hollywood stars, once said that a touch of red on navy, white on black is often the next best thing to a facelift!

The Impact Colours
These are the bright primaries of poppy red, emerald green and daffodil yellow, the exciting jewel colours of peacock and bright pink, purple and turquoise and, together, the drama of black and white. These are the eye-catching colours that make the fashion statement or the fun, witty accessories to the more subtle basics.

The Slimming Colours
The most slimming colours you can wear are those closest to the centre of the spectrum – green and blue. Green also strikes the eye at the point where it doesn't need to make an adjustment to look at it, which is why it is considered to be such a restful colour. Brighter, warm tones like red, yellow and orange make your figure appear larger, because they give the impression that it is actually nearer than is so, and the eye has to adjust. Cooler, more subtle colours make your figure appear to recede, although black gives the illusion of being heavy, can emphasize an outline and isn't such a slimming aid as often imagined. Select your clothes according to your figure type and colouring but bear in mind that the eye is attracted to the brightest of contrasting colours. Employ this to your advantage by choosing medium to dark neutrals on trouble-spot areas and use bright accent colours to attract the eye elsewhere.

Pattern Panache

● Mixing patterns together can be successful provided there is a continuous colour linking all the designs together. You only have to study the effect of Liberty prints used together to see how checks, florals and paisley can combine.

● Striking prints are better confined to a simple silhouette. Don't be tempted to clutter the outline with too many accessories. Jungle prints, for instance, make other patterns superfluous and may simply need a pair of bold earrings or a scarf in the hair to draw the eyes to the face.

● Patterns can be used as figure camouflage – wavy lines can add curves to a boyish figure, for instance – but if you aim to disguise bulk don't let the pattern become too eye-catching or you will defeat the purpose.

● Texture and pattern affect the colours we can wear. A

hard colour combination (say, bright yellow and black) can appear more flattering when the fabric has a sheen or lustre (silk or satin) or a texture (a knobbly tweed wool).

● Prints using dots, stripes or tiny geometric patterns can create dazzling optical effects and may be best confined to a small area.

Tips

● Colour is the best way to express your individuality and personality. Experiment with your own formula and you may be surprised at the variety it will bring to your basic outfits.

● Learn to reassess your colours as natural changes occur – for example a summer tan or greying hair. Your underlying skin tones don't change but your favourite shades may start to look hard or dull. Check colours that you may have overlooked and add new spice to your wardrobe.

● Remember that colours give messages and in some situations could be used to your advantage. Hot colours stimulate blood pressure, heartbeat and respiration and can be intimidating, softer warm colours can be inviting, cool colours can be businesslike or soft and relaxing.

When you look in your wardrobe, do you consider that your clothes are giving you value for money? On average, most women wear about 15 per cent of their wardrobe about 85 per cent of the time, proving that the real cost of clothes is not what we pay for them, but the division by the number of times we wear them. Reducing the quantity and being selective about what you buy is the basis for an organized wardrobe.

Not all good buys have to be expensive, but what you are looking for, and which often accounts for high pricing, is the excellence of design, cut and cloth. The kudos which comes from wearing well-made clothes will instil confidence and, because you will then be projecting a positive image, others will recognize this as successful dressing.

Projecting the right image for both business and social occasions has always been part of British tradition. We have a long and complicated history of sumptuary law (which imposed restraint on personal expenditure) dating back to the 12th century, when breaking a law, whether statutory or unspoken, made life economically and socially impossible. Today, with a very few exceptions, a more relaxed attitude prevails, though to avoid unnecessary antagonism, particularly in the work place, it helps to understand the language of clothes.

Wearing inappropriate clothes sends confused messages and doesn't inspire confidence. Anyone who fails to fit in with the occasion is always regarded with suspicion by the establishment. On the other hand, stamping your own personality on your clothes is essential, lest we all begin to look like clones! Individual touches can be as little as the texture of a jacket or the pattern of a scarf, but it will make a big difference to your own, and other people's, perception of you.

When organizing your wardrobe, and before you start adding to it, you must first be ruthless with the contents that are already there. Once you have pared down to the best items, subsequent buys will become investments for your lifestyle.

Ruthless Revamp!

● To make your wardrobe really functional, you should aim for hanging space where clothes are not wedged in so tightly that you can't easily see what you have. First, go through your clothes and weed out items that you haven't worn for over a year, maybe because they don't fit properly, are looking dated, or were a mistaken buy in the first place. Check to see if any easy alterations will make them work again (narrowing wide-leg trousers or shortening a long evening dress to cocktail length); otherwise, get rid of them.

● Dispose of anything that doesn't fit in with your lifestyle now – long skirts that were fine in the hippy era but don't go with city pavements or public transport; scuffed or scruffy shoes; ankle boots if you have short legs; belts that are too small for your waist; long velvet evening skirts if you prefer evening dresses; a print blouse you bought in a sale that makes you look vast. Learn from your mistakes.

● Never keep anything in your wardrobe that isn't wearable. Do any mending jobs immediately and put dirty clothes directly into the linen basket for washing.

● Separate clothes in your best colour spectrum from those in colours that aren't your ideal. Over the years you can replace the 'wrong' colours, but meanwhile compromise by wearing a 'wrong' coloured suit with a blouse that compliments your colouring or 'wrong' coloured trousers with a 'right' sweater. Even a 'wrong' coloured coat can be worn with a scarf that suits you. Alternatively, try to find a few friends who have different colouring and who may be willing to do an exchange!

● Hang similar items together and split suits into the relevant jacket or skirt section so that they can be worn as separates.

● Hang black clothes inside out to prevent them picking up dust and fluff.

● Invest in some decent hangers and throw away those wire ones, which can make clothes look misshapen.

● To hang up a long evening dress without the hem touching the floor, sew loops at waist level and hang it inside out, like a skirt.

● Make use of multiple hangers for scarves and belts and, if you are short of space, pack away out-of-season clothes.

● Fold sweaters and knitted dresses (stretchable items) and store on shelves or in drawers.

● Put trousers over hangers that have well-padded bars to prevent ugly crease marks.

Wardrobe Analysis

When you are working out how to add to and improve on your current collection of clothes, ask yourself a few fundamental questions. How do you spend your time and where and what are your priorities? Do you work? Do you entertain much? Do you attend meetings, charity events, lunches or dinners? Does your husband's job impinge on your life? Are you involved in school functions? Do you require outfits for speech day, sports day, weddings? Do you travel on business or strictly for holidays? Do you live in the town, visit restaurants? Do you live in the country? Do you find food shopping, housework and children take up most of your time? Do you have much leisure time or belong to a sports club? Your lifestyle will obviously dictate what your wardrobe should contain.

Shopping Tips

● Determine what you need and invest in the clothes you will be wearing the most. Even if much of your life is spent in jeans, make sure they are well-cut and that you have several pairs.

● If you don't go out socializing very often you won't want to direct much of your budget into evening clothes. Find one basic dress in a beautiful fabric which can be dressed up or down with updated accessories from year to year.

● As you live in a cool climate your biggest investment will be on outerwear. You need one good winter coat, a heavyweight and a lightweight casual jacket, a winter and a summer raincoat. Take your time when there is a lot of money at stake.

● Don't wait until the last minute to shop for a 'special occasion' item since you risk not finding exactly what you need and will probably end up with something disappointing that doesn't get worn again.

● Never go shopping if you are feeling depressed! This is when you buy clothes on a whim, and they are invariably mistaken buys.

● Sales can work to your advantage. Look for expensive clothing that has genuine reductions. There is no bargain if it doesn't work for you or the fit is just a little bit tight but the price irresistible. Ask yourself if you really need it. Is it the right shape and colour for you? Will it fit into your lifestyle? If the answer is yes to all these questions, then buy it!

● Perversely, winter stock starts filtering into the shops in August and summer stock in February. During the very months when you don't need them the best selection of styles is available. This is essential knowledge if you are not a standard size and generally need more choice. At the same time, check out the sales which precede the new stock arrival as they are usually selling exactly the right thing for the seasonal weather.

● Buy the best you can afford. A couple of lambswool or cashmere sweaters in your best colours are a better investment than six acrylic ones for the same amount of money, since apart from lasting longer and looking better (acrylic fibres often have a harsh quality in the dye colour), the initial expense is justified by the confidence given by wearing the best.

● Coordinated separates shopping is made easy for you

when the ranges are all displayed in a group. This can be a convenient way to invest in several pieces that work well together as the designer planned. Make sure that the colour schemes fall in with your ideals and that the silhouettes work for your shape. Don't be pressurized into buying items you might not wear much just because they 'match'.

● When you buy a single item like a skirt which needs a particular blouse or shoes to go with it try to buy them on the same day, otherwise you risk the skirt becoming redundant for quite some time while you look for something that coordinates.

● If you find a particular blouse or shirt that has got the perfect proportions for you, buy it in several of your colourways. The same goes for shoes. If they are the perfect shape and heel height, buy a couple of pairs in basic colours. These are time-saving investments.

● Avoid a tacky buy. A good quality garment will be made from a high percentage of natural fibre. Check the zip, which should be the correct weight for the fabric and well concealed, closing neatly at the top. Look at the lining, which should be soft and roomy. Make sure seams aren't ragged. Check that patterns match at the side seams. If there is top-stitching, is it even and straight? Are hems invisible, with no hanging threads, and are buttonholes properly finished off? Check that the buttons align with their corresponding holes.

● Budget buys work too. Another woman's mistaken buy could be your gain, provided you remember all the ground rules and don't buy just because the price is reasonable. Keep an eye open for bargains in the second-hand shops and jumble sales. An instant trick for upmarketing a dress or blouse is to sew on expensive buttons of your choice – and always substitute a classy leather belt for one made from self fabric.

● Learn about fit. Know the difference between too small, as in tight, and snug, as in a knit top which is supposed to be close fitting. Know the difference between oversized, as in perfectly loose, and just plain enormous, as in the wrong size. *Never* let a salesperson talk you into it. If in doubt, don't buy!

Making Your Clothes Work For You

Building up a basic wardrobe is easy once you've determined the perfect proportions for your shape, your most flattering colours and the styles which best suit your personality – though the variety of clothes will depend on your budget, your lifestyle and your inclination to follow fashion trends. None of us can be immune to fashion, and even a classic

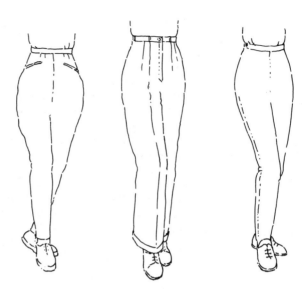

Jodhpurs, Oxford Bags and Ski-pants are fine for the well-proportioned

Classic straight leg

Side zips flatter the stomach

Peg tops flatter small waists

Elasticated waists are comfortable

Too tight jeans flatter nobody

good buy like a beautifully cut trenchcoat can have its proportions influenced by the prevailing styles. When a new and often eccentric look hits the designer catwalks the watered-down high street versions are fast to follow. The eye quickly adapts to the new lines and proportions and thus something that a few years before would have been unthinkable becomes fresh, novel and desirable. This is where your personal style will enter into it. Only you will be able to determine whether such a style will become part of your basic wardrobe, and whether you will be able to wear it a number of different ways on numerous occasions.

Good accessories are essential and often make the difference between the mediocre and stunning. Without some form of fashionable appeal clothes can look dated, so keep your eye on the fashion magazines and look at the window displays in the shops to gain ideas. Only the young can get away with extremes in fashion, but there's no reason why others shouldn't have fun too!

Clothes For Your Lifestyle

Once you have established the type of clothes your lifestyle requires the next stop is to narrow down the choice within the different sections.

Casual Occasions

Casual clothes don't mean sloppy clothes, so even if your only human contacts during the day are the postman or a neighbour don't neglect your looks.

Trousers epitomize relaxed, comfortable dressing and the trick is to find the shape that suits you best.

● Always try on trousers using a rear view mirror as well as a front one, since the cut and fit are crucial and trousers which are badly fitting or too tight will only accentuate your weight.

● If you are well proportioned you can get away with styles like jodhpurs, Oxford bags or ski pants, but the majority of people suit the classic straight-leg trouser with side pockets and two soft front pleats. If your knickerline shows, they are too tight!

● To reduce the hipline, choose fabrics that don't add bulk. Avoid heavy cords or tweeds and choose flannel, gabardine, jersey and silk.

● Tight jeans may appear to be keeping in all the bulges but after a while horizontal stress lines appear in the fabric, emphasizing the very parts best skimmed over.

● Trouser lengths should just break on the foot, unless the style is deliberately chopped off at the calf. Remember, cutoffs and turn-ups will effectively shorten the leg.

● A side zipper gives a flatter line across the stomach.

● A peg-top waist (a belted high waist) is best for tiny waists. It lengthens the legline but emphasizes a short torso or big bust.

● A drawstring or elasticated waistline is great for the active person or one whose waistline keeps fluctuating. It is certainly the most comfortable style but can be shapeless around the hip and crutch area.

Knitwear is the easy answer as a partner for trousers and it comes in all shapes and textures, from a classic V-necked lambswool cardigan to the crunchiest, most intricate designer sweater.

● Always follow washing instructions carefully and you'll find quality knitwear will give good returns season after season. Inexpensive sweaters pill when washed and quickly look tatty.

● Designer kits to knit yourself are good news for anyone with nimble fingers and will save you pounds.

● Fairisle patterns are a classic buy and look best in the traditional soft colours of the Scottish islands.

● The easiest sweaters to wear are those with a neckline that needs nothing else with it, for example a polo or a cowl (though not for the short-necked).

● V-necked and collared, button-front sweaters are good necklines to flatter a softened jawline, round face or short neck.

Long lean sweater line flatters a rounded figure

V-necks flatter round faces and soft fairish colours flatter the fair

Cowl necks are not for short necks

Mohair is soft and appealing for the slim

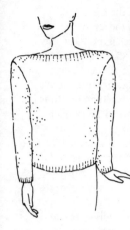

Slash necks and shoulder pads help give width to sloping shoulders

● Bulky, textured knitwear invariably adds inches to the overweight, so stick to flatter, thinner yarns in long, lean styles.

● Cotton knitwear is perfect for indoors when wool sweaters are too warm with winter central heating. They are ideal for cool summer evenings too.

● Sew in shoulder pads if you have sloping or narrow shoulders or if a sweater needs extra shaping.

● Men's sweaters can look wonderful on women and often provide the extra roominess and length that is flattering to all but the very petite.

Business Occasions

I believe the backbone of any business wardrobe is a good selection of interchangeable separates in practical, hard-wearing fabrics. Although neat efficiency in dressing suggests a businesslike approach to work this will only suit the truly classic dresser who will always look superb in a tailored style. Soften the look or add drama, according to your personality.

For a successful working wardrobe choose a basic colour theme like navy, beige, black or grey and use this for major items like an overcoat and suit. Ring the colour changes with crisp shirts and pretty blouses or classic sweaters. Use splashes of bright colour or witty accessories to prevent classic lines from becoming boring.

Dramatic business dressing

● A smart blazer is an essential look for summer dressing and works well with a white pleated skirt or dress.

● White or pale shirts always look crisp teamed with a dark suit, even if they are made from a soft fabric.

● Don't overdo the accessories. Clanking bracelets can be irritating and won't impress at a serious meeting.

● When attending an important meeting leave your hand-bag behind and just take your briefcase – which should be the best you can afford.

● Offices are often either overheated or too cool from air-conditioning. Layer dressing will enable you to take off or add on, depending on your circumstances.

● Don't wear blouses made from fabrics so thin that your bra shows through in an obvious manner.

● Don't feel you have to wear something different each day. Men don't.

Smart Occasions

Being smart means dressing to suit the occasion so that you feel neither over nor underdressed, and both physically

Hat and gloves for panache

comfortable and mentally confident. If you have bought an outfit for a particular occasion, don't leave it to the last minute to try it out with all the accessories. You may decide a dress needs higher heels, for instance, or that your hat isn't quite the right colour after all. Get used to wearing your complete outfit and then you will feel perfectly at ease with it on the day. Don't forget the weather may play an important part in your choice of jacket or coat. Check that the hem of your dress or skirt isn't longer than the coat, and that you have an umbrella that goes with the colour scheme if it looks like rain. Avoid a wrap-style skirt or dress that might flap in the wind and reveal more than intended.

When I go somewhere special, I think about my outfit from my feet upwards. I never wear very high heels if I am going to be doing a lot of walking about, nor do I wear flimsy shoes if I am likely to be treading on rough ground or if it is pouring with rain. I do, however, always spray good leather shoes with a weather protection spray before going out, having once ruined a beautiful and expensive pair of shoes by walking along petrol-soaked, dirty pavements in a thunderstorm. I also never drive in good shoes because the backs of the heels become scuffed; I keep an old pair of flatties in the car for that purpose. If I shall be stepping out of a car and into a restaurant, for instance, I know I am relatively safe to wear higher heels, and from there I am able to decide what else to wear.

Formal events such as weddings, christenings and grand society occasions demand that extra bit of effort with the details to give a special effect. Look for a dress or dress and jacket in an elegant, simple design made from luxury fabrics like silk or linen mix; add a hat for panache, gloves and appropriate jewellery. Keep the hat in proportion with your body – the taller you are, the wider the brim can be – and either match up a colour exactly or choose a contrast shade if you want to create impact.

Less formal occasions such as a school speech day or a meeting with your bank manager mean you can team every day separates with a silk shirt and an understated straw hat or turban. The finishing touches are always important because they give a good top-to-toe impression.

essing-up
eryday separates

● **Hat trick:** You can add your own trims to a basic hat shape and make it appear different for each outing. All you need is an artificial flower, a beautiful feather or some snazzy ribbon from a local haberdashery.

A glamorous ballgown

Glamorous Occasions

The demarcation between day and evening dressing is being constantly eroded, particularly as office to evening functions often don't allow for a stopover at home to change outfits. This is where a change of jewellery, from discreet to ritzy, and a glamorous pair of shoes can help ring the changes for someone pressed for time.

Costume jewellery need not cost the earth. Beautiful necklaces and diamanté brooches abound in antique market stalls and are a fraction of the price of their modern-day counterparts. While you are scouting, look out for beautiful lace collars which can be sewn on to a plain black dress, a finely embroidered shawl which could wrap around the shoulders of an otherwise bare neckline, or some delicately crocheted gloves. Make your own layers of net petticoat to puff out full skirts and transform a plain court shoe with your own trims. You can buy fancy diamanté buckles and bows and they can be used as hair decorations too.

For the grand ball or social occasion that needs a full-length gown pull out all the stops, choosing luxurious fabrics like lace and satin, silk, brocade, taffeta and velvet. Alternatively, you may decide that for a one-off event it would be less expensive to hire a gown. Second-hand shops are also a good source for original ballgowns and then your only real outlay would be for jewellery. As a general rule of thumb, the more patterned and elaborate the fabric of the dress the less jewellery you will need.

Unless you have a diary full of grand social events evening dresses are usually disproportionately expensive for the amount of wear they will receive, hence the emergence of the 'little black dress'. A beautifully cut, plain style in a flattering silhouette can be worn season after season with a change of accessories without it being obvious that it is the same dress. Of course, it doesn't have to be black – it could just as easily be dark red, but it will be the accessories which will help you stamp your style on a basic shape.

Party trick: Use lengths of satin ribbon for special effects. Tie ribbon around your neck, bow to the front, and pin on a spectacular brooch; tie it with bow at the back and let the streamers hang down a backless dress. Use a wide ribbon as a very feminine waist sash. Tiny bows of ribbon look pretty in the hair, tied among pearls, on a bracelet or on shoes (but not altogether!)

Sporting Occasions

Whether you are a spectator or an active participant, dressing for the part makes sense. Standing around a draughty golf course in a cold wind is no fun for either the supporter or the player, and neither is school sports day when it's pouring with rain. For anyone obliged to be on the sidelines, keeping warm and weatherproof is the essential thing, while the player must concentrate on practical clothing which will stand the wear and tear of her particular sport.

The stylish spectator

The Spectator: For the great outdoors and the unpredictable weather, investing in a warm, casual, shower-proof jacket goes without saying, though just as important are footwear and headwear. A surprising amount of heat is lost through the head, so cover up with a scarf or an appropriate hat. Trilbies always look stylish and can be worn with most outfits, though they look best with riding macs or jackets made from waxed cotton, suedes or denim. Padded jackets inspired by the ski slopes look better with bright knitted bandeaux, and at times look incongruous in country surroundings. Soft, earthy colours will be more in harmony with a rural setting such as a gymkhana, but harsh, bright shades may well suit a sophisticated race meeting.

Nothing makes you feel more miserable than soggy socks or soaked shoes so, depending on the sort of ground you will be stationed at, think flat, think tough, think practical. Waterproofed boots don't have to be wellie-shaped, but always buy them big enough to accommodate two pairs of thin socks – your insulation against the cold. Thick, textured tights are fashionable assets, especially in country colours, and look wonderful with lace-up shoes and a sheepskin jacket. If it is really chilly use thermal underwear and shawls to give extra layers of warmth and choose warm-coloured clothing to counter that blue feeling!

Of course, not all sports take place outdoors, or in bad weather. At Wimbledon, for instance, you are more likely to need a brimmed hat and suntan lotion as your essental accessories. Social occasions such as the Henley Regatta or Cowes Week call for much more elegant dressing – even a witty, nautical theme in navy and white – and are far removed from the actual practicalities of a sailing enthusiast, who would be much more concerned with wearing non-slip deck shoes than sporting an outfit with a sailor collar.

Sporty stripes

The Sporty: Fitness is the spin-off from sport, although not all activities have to be strenuous. Walking is a popular leisure pursuit, especially if you can take advantage of the countryside, and all you need are sturdy walking shoes and some comfortable casual wear.

Golf can be a relaxed affair, though tradition calls for divided skirts and classic argyle sweaters. Lightweight casual wear – a blouson jacket and trousers or a pleated skirt – look fresh for summer but the main criterion is that the upper body has ease of movement for the perfect swing.

Sailing buffs need more specialist clothing such as oilskins or nylon ciré jackets to protect them from the elements, and there are sailing boots with drawstring tops for when the going gets rough. In the sun, though, T-shirts (striped navy and white matelot tops are popular) and cotton drill trousers, shorts or jeans come into their own.

Running has gained in popularity in recent years, though not everyone is aiming for the marathon. Whether you're running races or jogging around the local park, proper running shoes are essential. A sports bra, towelling socks and loose, comfortable clothing are your other needs. Track suits have passed into fashion history but their imprint is still in evidence, proving that practical styles needn't be mundane.

Tennis is another sport for the active, and although it is more popular during summer months there is also scope for indoor practice. Again, shoes are of paramount importance but expensive tennis shirts and skirts emblazoned with special logos are not essential to the game. T-shirts and shorts are perfectly practical, although a tennis dress or pleated skirt is generally more feminine and flattering.

For the very energetic, skiing offers an occasional foray into the mountains and a chance to be stylish in the snow. Initial clothing is expensive, so try to borrow clothes if you are a beginner. Cheapest buys are a padded jacket (make sure it has zipped pockets, a hood which tucks away into the neckline, and zip-out sleeves as a useful option) and salopettes (which are similar to slinky dungarees), worn with thermal underwear in extreme conditions. The jacket will always be useful should you decide skiing isn't for you. All-in-one suits are a comfortable alternative and are generally more slimming in design. The extras such as goggles, gloves, and hats push the price up. Boots and skis can be hired at the resorts so don't bother with your own equipment unless you are a regular skier. Après-ski wear is usually casual (tops and trousers are most useful) and, like the ski wear, is bright and fun.

In complete contrast, swimming is a year-round pursuit which, for as little as the price of a swimsuit, acts as a terrific tone-up for the body. For a public pool, the swimsuit needs to be strictly functional – save the fancy designs for your holiday. The choice is vast, but the sleek racing lines with T-backs or straps crossed at the back look good. Choose a style with a fairly high cut legline to elongate your legs and with vertical lines for a slimming effect. Use goggles and a swimcap to protect against the chlorine in the pool.

Holiday Occasions

The art of not over-packing for holidays is always to carry your own case. In this way I have, over the years, pared down my own luggage to the bare essentials! It's always best to stick with a basic colour scheme and white or cream is as good as any when it comes to a hot country. Take clothes that are multi-purpose (shorts which will double for the beach and for sightseeing, for instance) and that will inter-match with other items. Lay everything on the bed before you pack to make sure you have no joker in the pack!

Take a pair of shorts, a pair of trousers, a skirt, a T-shirt dress and two T-shirts, all in your basic pale colour. Then add a long-sleeved shirt, a couple of other tops which will coordinate, a patterned sundress, a cotton sweater, your bikinis, swimsuit, towels, sunglasses and a kanga cover-up. Travel in elasticated waist trousers or skirt, T-shirt or short-sleeved shirt and a lightweight jacket. I find clothes made from cotton jersey T-shirt fabric most useful, since they roll up for easy packing and don't crease. Reinforced nylon holdall bags are ideal for lightening the load.

Holiday tips for a successful trip are:

Holiday separates

> ● Don't pack a lot of jewellery, since the heat makes it uncomfortable to wear except in the evening.
> ● Take several styles of swimsuits and bikinis so that you can avoid strapmarks marring your tan.
> ● Make full use of the backless styles to show off a good tan.
> ● Don't wear metal jewellery on the beach because it acts as a conductor for the heat and can burn your skin.
> ● Pack inexpensive pull-on pumps for the beach and throw them away before you go home.
> ● Depending on where you go and how you like to spend your time, pack one item specifically for evening wear – but since most holidays are for relaxing, casual wear should have priority.
> ● The kanga will be one of the most useful items in your suitcase since it acts like a multi-purpose dress, wrapping around the body in a number of ways.
> ● Swimsuit or bikini, choose the most flattering shape for your figure.

Bikini Lore: If you are big hipped choose a medium colour, narrow at the sides but with enough material in the pants not to make them look skimpy. A halter strapline will give the illusion of wider shoulders (good to balance a pear-shaped body.) If you have a big bust, choose a style with light underwiring for support. Choose pants with a high cut leg to give the illusion of longer legs. If you are slim you can wear frills, top and bottom. Bandeau bikinis are not for the big-bosomed and are not recommended for playing beach games in for obvious reasons!

Swimsuit Sense: Never wear a too-small swimsuit. Tell-tale signs are straps that dig into shoulders, a flattened bustline and a yanked-up crutch. All-in-one suits in plain colours or with clever use of patterning are generally more flattering for larger figures. Horizontal stripes add width and curve, vertical stripes slim and lengthen. Cut-away leg lines are very flattering but ensure that the suit isn't too cut-away at the rear if this isn't your best feature. If a rounded tummy is your problem, choose a suit with design interest on the top.

5

ACCESSORIES

In my view, accessories play one of the most vital roles when it comes to stamping your own identity on an outfit. The impression can be muted, a good taste mix of classy jewellery and understated leather belt and shoes; exuberant, with overstated fake jewellery and other 'notice-me' extras; or a mixture of the unexpected which has the effect of lifting an ordinary outfit into a stylish one. Much will depend on your mood, your personality and the type of clothes that you feel happiest wearing. A natural person, for instance, would probably not be at home wearing diamanté earrings with denim, while a dramatic person would thrive on such an unlikely combination. Generally speaking, accessories are an ideal way of adding colour, wit, class, glitz or simply the finishing touches to your basic outfit and they offer great scope for creativity.

It's worth spending some time experimenting with different looks and studying the results in a full-length mirror for top-to-toe impact. Ask yourself if the proportions look right. Is there too much going on or not enough? If you are at all doubtful about wearing too much jewellery take some away. It's better to have too little than too much. The final test is that you do not feel awkward or showy. You must feel completely comfortable with your entire outfit and therefore confident that you are looking your best.

Jewellery

Adding the right piece of jewellery can make or mar an outfit. If you have spent a lot of money on a dress or a suit, it makes sense to add some classy accessories and real jewellery is an investment which never dates. Gold will suit warm skin tones and silver will suit cool ones and, although expensive, the real thing will not be an extravagance in terms of cost per wear.

A simple gold or silver chain and matching classic earrings will add class to any outfit, and from then on the occasion and your personality will dictate how bold you will be. Traditionally, drop earrings, stone settings, diamanté and crystal have been worn in the evenings or for grand occasions, but nowadays anything goes. Pearls look good for day or evening wear, and for less formal occasions fakes come in strings of pastel colours or giant sizes for fun. Colourful plastics are useful for splashes of colour and generally look good with more casual clothes, while flashy paste jewellery can add fun to understated outfits. Back in the thirties Coco Chanel showed how costume jewellery could be as stylish as the real thing, and her legacy of gilt and pearl earclips and ropes of glass and pearls still looks good with fashions today. For most period panache, check out antique fairs and second-hand shops for unusual gems. Brooches and earrings in particular can be real bargain buys.

Real jewellery can also mean natural accessories made from horn, wood, coral, leather, mother-of-pearl and antique ivory – all of which look wonderful mixed in with gold or silver or semi-precious stones and minerals such as lapis lazuli, tiger-eye, quartz, copper and jade. Collectables such as these help to ring the changes when you wear a basic outfit. Imagine a pale two-piece made ethnic with carved wood and ivory bracelets, made feminine with shiny mother-of-pearl earrings and necklace, or made elegant with gold chains.

Watches are an important accessory and can range from an expensive Rolex to a fun Swatch. Unless you want a wardrobe of watches stay with a classic gold or silver bracelet design or a straightforward one which incorporates a leather strap in a basic colour. Choose a watch in proportion with your frame; small-boned, petite women look best with a smaller, dainty watch; curvy women look best with round or oval faced watches. Fun watches with unusual faces or coloured straps look great with holiday clothes, are often inexpensive and water-resistant and are a good buy if you are planning a beach holiday.

Jewellery Gems

● Rings draw attention to your hands, so only wear them if your fingers are long and shapely and you have presentable nails. Otherwise, keep rings plain and simple.

● Some metals can cause skin allergies, so if wristwatches cause you a problem try a clip-on version or hang one medal-style from a breast pocket. A pendant or an old-fashioned fob watch are alternatives.

● The plainer your dress or outfit is the more jewellery you can wear. The 'pile-it-on' philosophy works particularly well with ethnic necklaces and also pearls.

● Avoid wearing dangly earrings or choker-style necklaces if you have a short neck.

● A 16-inch (41cm) necklace is about the right length for open-necked shirts, while longer styles will help to elongate a neckline.

● Jewellery helps to focus attention on a particular area, so use it to your advantage. If, for instance, you have a big bust, wear unusual earrings or pin a brooch around the shoulder area to attract the eye away from the areas that you prefer to go unnoticed.

Belts At their most functional, they loop through skirts and trousers and add a shapely finishing touch. At their most decorative, belts can give stunning emphasis to the waist or hips using a remarkable array of materials and buckle detail. Eye-catching belts are expensive but one exciting belt can lift a plain-looking dress into a different league, whereas a cheap belt will ruin the effect. The easiest way to upgrade an inexpensive outfit is to replace a fabric belt with a leather belt or to choose a belt with a beautiful buckle.

Always choose a belt in keeping with the general feeling of the outfit. Soft suedes and leathers which wrap and knot look good with soft fabrics such as corduroy, tweeds and jerseys. A stiffer leather suits a stiffer fabric like gabardine or cotton drill. A no-nonsense, classic buckle, snakeskin or leather, looks good with a business suit, while the more ornate styles will add zing to casuals and evening wear. Ethnic styles suggest rough, tough leather, thonging and beading, chamois, metal and rope, webbing and other natural fibres; formal clothes call for smooth, classic leathers and suedes with beautiful top-stitching. Silks, velvets and tapestry, patent and special finishes on leather look good for evening clothes.

Fashion rules are meant to be broken, however, and some of the least likely combinations offer an exciting alternative to the conventional mode of dress. Experimentation is the key. Try a complete change of fabric weight and combine the rough with the smooth by wearing a tough-look leather belt wrapped around a chiffon skirt, or wear a glitzy evening belt with a grey flannel city suit. Improvise with your own ideas. Wear two or three belts at once, or wear a thin belt over a wide belt. Use a length of chain, rope or cord to make your own simple belt, knotted and twisted according to your fancy. Fake skins are dramatic and move in and out of fashion fairly regularly, so watch the magazines for the latest looks.

Tips
● Belt width must not be determined by fashion but by your proportions. Thus, if you are petite, don't choose chunky wide belts in contrast colours which will only serve to break up your body shape and make you appear smaller.
● If you have a small waist, always belt it to make the most of it. If you aren't slim, never belt up too tightly and avoid extra-wide belts which could emphasize bulges.
● Belts slung on the hips help to elongate the body but will also draw attention to this area. Toning belts add shape, contrast belts add emphasis.
● Square, rectangular and geometric belt buckles are best

with uncluttered, straight styles; ovals and curves compliment a softer line; circles, swirls and flowered buckles enhance flowing, curvy styles.

Handbags Since your handbags are an indispensible item and will consequently receive a lot of wear and tear, it is worth buying the best you can afford. Leather is hardwearing and tends to improve with age, so provided you choose a fairly classic shape in a basic colour it's a worthwhile investment. Look at your wardrobe and decide what basic colours would be most useful to tone in with your clothes. Cool clear and cool muted colourings suggest black, white, grey or navy, while warm clear and warm muted colourings suggest ivory, beiges, browns and tans. For light relief, casual occasions and holidays, canvas satchels and duffle bags in fun colours are a good inexpensive buy.

The overriding need is to choose a bag which echoes the same line and scale as your clothes, emphasizing angles or complimenting curves. Thus a dramatic or classic dresser who would suit the straighter lines should choose handbags that are square or rectangular and precisely constructed from firm materials. The natural and romantic dressers should look for softer lines, ideally choosing leather pouches with small gathers or with rounded or curved details.

Of course, the scale of the bag should not overwhelm your outfit. A petite figure would look unbalanced carrying a huge tote bag, just as a tall figure would look silly carrying a tiny clutch bag. Adjust according to your needs, but keep everything in proportion.

Tips
● Before buying a new bag check that it will hold everything you are likely to need. Businesswomen may find that their planner or diary is too bulky for a conventional handbag, so a small briefcase may be needed as well.
● Always buy the best briefcase you can afford for your professional life. This gives out the message that you are successful and that you rate yourself highly.
● Leather handbags respond to polish and protective sprays, just like shoes. Look after your investment!
● If you are hip heavy, adjust the strap of a shoulder bag so that it hangs at the top of your hipbone.
● Don't carry unnecessary clutter in your handbag. It merely weighs your shoulder down and gives an unbalanced look.
● If you have to carry a lot of keys, pens or small change, choose a bag with zipped sections or extra pockets so that these items are readily accessible.

● Second-hand shops and antique fairs are a wonderful source for small beaded evening bags, which were popular in the twenties and thirties. They are wonderful value and often need only very minor repairs.

Hats

Sophisticated toque

Classic brim

The Trilby

ce-framing hats

al saucer hat

Ever since the Princess of Wales added her stamp of approval to the millinery world hats have assumed renewed importance on the fashion front. Not just for weddings and grand society occasions but for everyday wear, hats are steadily gaining in popularity. Like everything else in your wardrobe they must lend themselves to your lifestyle, face, figure and hairstyle, so first of all try on as many styles as possible in order to find a flattering silhouette.

Always check the overall impression in a full-length mirror, wearing the outfit you intend the hat to match. Does the hat fit properly? The crown should be a snug fit and the brim should never be wider than your shoulders. Proportions suggest that a petite woman looks best in a scaled-down hat and a taller person can take a wide brim or a hat with an extravagant trim.

Sophisticated styles such as turbans or toques often look good with hair swept back or neatly tucked back off the face altogether. They suit the uncluttered lines of the dramatic and classic dresser. Trilbies, panamas and most brimmed straws suit most face shapes and casual or smart hairstyles; they look good on natural and classic dressers, while berets, the floppy-brimmed straws and brimmed felts look particularly good on long-haired romantics. Bows, silk flowers, feathers and wispy net trims are just made for the romantics, while glitzy decorations and strong veiling will suit the dramatics. The most important thing is to get the basic shape right, then you can add or subtract trims as you like.

Tips
● Providing the shape suits your face, be guided by your outfit as to which hat-style looks good. A dress with a sailor collar may go well with a boater or a Basque beret; a city suit may need a trilby; a waisted jacket and swinging skirt will look good with a stylish toque; a soft jersey suit may be complimented by a turban; a floral dress may demand a straw with a floral trim.
● Enhance your face shape with a hat. A face-framing halo brim looks good on all but the very round-faced; such faces are elongated with upswept hats or toques or diverted by small saucer shapes. Long faces should avoid these elongating styles and concentrate on brims which draw the eye outwards.

Exotic turban

● Designer hats are beautifully made but expensive. Look and learn from their designs, then purchase a good basic shape from a chain store and invent your own trims.
● Look after your hats. Keep a good shape by stuffing the crown with tissue and store in a hat box.

Scarves

Scarves soften severe lines, add pattern and texture to outfits and are a marvellous way of bringing flattering colours to your face. Highly collectable are long, skinny silk scarves, squares of satin or printed silk, squares of gossamer lacy wool shawls, large square cashmere or wool wraps and cashmere mufflers.

Knotted scarf necklace

Small scarves can be worn at the neck in a variety of ways and by all but the very short-necked. Larger shawls add an extra layer of warmth and dash, while the patterns and colour can coordinate an entire outfit. Tall, dramatic personalities carry off the sweeping large shawls while classics go for the long mufflers and Grace Kelly head squares. Naturals love the cotton, sporty scarves and romantics suit the drape and softness of silk.

Tips

Twisted scarf

● Fold a thin square scarf on the bias, tie knots at regular intervals and use as a necklace or belt.
● Using a long muffler or skinny scarf, fold it in half and wrap around your neck, pulling the ends through the loop formed by the fold.
● For a cravat with a difference, tie a knot in the centre of a square silk scarf. Keeping the knot on the underside and at the front, tie two opposite corners around your neck at the back. Tuck the front of the scarf into your neckline.

Cravat knot

● For a pretty fan effect, take a large square scarf and fold it back and forth into concertina pleats, so that you finally have one narrow strip. Hold the ends so that the pleating won't spring apart, wrap the scarf around your neck and tie once in front. Secure with a brooch and tease out the ends of the fan to the side.
● Twist a long, multi-coloured scarf into a rope and wrap around your neck twice. Bring the ends to the front and secure by tucking over and under in an abstract knot.

Fan scarf

Shoes   I am a great hoarder of shoes and therefore am always surprised when friends seem to manage with three or four basic pairs. Much of your footwear will depend on the life you lead and the clothes you wear, but for sheer value for money the leather court shoe comes off best. With a medium heel and a good toe shape that won't date, it can be worn with dresses, skirts, smarter trousers and, with the addition of shoe bows, for the evening occasion too. Once you have found a court shoe that fits you well, buy the same style in a light and dark neutral shade and they will carry you effortlessly through the season. If much of your time is spent in casual clothes, invest in some comfortable trainers and flat brogues or loafers, ringing the changes with canvas pumps or plimsolls during the summer.

Leather shoes and boots are a worthwhile investment because, if you look after them well, they look good for a long time and allow your feet to 'breathe'. However, synthetic materials come into their own on rainy days when you don't want to ruin good footwear. Boots are expensive, so choose a classic style that won't date easily. Stay clear of the 'here today, gone tomorrow' fashion gimmicks – very pointed toes, lots of tassels or cowboy styles (unless you wear a lot of denim). Whether leather or synthetic, all shoes and boots benefit from shoe trees, which help them maintain their shape, and, of course, a regular polish. Buy a neutral polish which is perfect for all colours and before wearing a new pair of shoes spray them with a rain protector product.

Tips
A slim medium heel and a low-cut toe shape will help to elongate the foot. Too high a heel makes the calf muscles too prominent so that short legs look even shorter and heavy legs look heavier.
● To make legs look longer, avoid T-straps, wide inset straps and ankle straps. High-laced shoes and bootees effectively shorten the foot and only look good with trousers.
● Use a full-length mirror to check the overall balance of your outfit with your shoes. You don't have to match shoes to what you are wearing – they can be a contrast colour which may be echoed in a scarf, for instance, but it then helps to tone your tights colour accordingly and to keep the contrast from leg to shoe from being too abrupt.
● White shoes can be as stark as black, and attract the eye to your feet, so only wear them if you are lean and long-legged.
● Don't be down-at-heel. Get shoes heeled and soled regularly.

Legwear Not since the sixties has there been such an upsurge of different hose to choose from – opaque and textured tights to keep us warm in the winter, colourful sheers for smart occasions, witty motif and patterned tights for fun, alluring metallics for parties and sexy black sheers and lacy looks for sophisticated evening wear. Some styles will appeal more than others – patterned tights, for instance, usually only look good on the youthful, long, lean leg. Horizontal stripes will only suit skinny legs and pale spots or small patterns sometimes look more like a skin disease than a smart pair of tights. Dark dotty tights, lacy tights, fishnets and all the coloured tights, however, look good on most legs. Tights with vertical lines or a back seam are generally slimming, though some textured tights are not. If you wish to draw attention to your legs and make them a feature, you have plenty of options open to you. If you are heavy-legged however, the more discreet neutrals with a toning shoe are the best disguise and help to elongate the leg.

Tips
● **Bulk-buy neutral-coloured tights which tone with your clothes, since these will be the most useful to you.** Some sheer tights give an added contour to your leg, others give a more even colour distribution.
● **Denier is the hosiery term for density** – the lower the figure, the finer the hose.
● **If you have shapely ankles look out for hose which have a bow motif at the ankle.**
● Warm, textured tights vary a great deal in thickness, so if your legs are on the heavy side and you don't want to add bulk, do select carefully.
● **Stockings are more hygienic to wear than tights since they allow air to circulate more freely.** However, tights give a smoother line, are more comfortable and are warmer in the winter. The choice is yours!
● Wash your tights after every wear – it restores their elasticity.
● **Support tights now come in fine deniers and are a boon as camouflage for varicose veins or blemished legs.**
● Pop socks are useful under trousers and are ideal for travelling from a cool to a hot climate as they can be easily removed.
● **Some tights now have built-in panties, which are ideal for a smooth line under trousers or a slimline dress.**

Extras   It's often the small details which prevent a straightforward classic outfit from looking ordinary. For instance, if you are wearing a basic navy coat with toning tights and shoes, use a scarf to give a splash of colour at the neckline and then add brightly coloured leather gloves for fun. Gloves are an inexpensive way of adding small amounts of colour as well as finishing off an outfit. Pocket handkerchiefs are also invaluable for the same reason. A beautiful lacy hanky emerging from a tailored jacket is a wonderfully feminine touch and a good contrast of textures. Hair bows, instead of hats, have sleek appeal without the formality, and shoe bows can add a frivolous touch to a plain shoe. If you want to steal ideas from the men's department, wear a tie to the office. It will look classsic with a pinstriped shirt, but more feminine with a silk blouse. Contrast a lace cravat with a formal shirt, a pretty lace top with a tailored leather skirt, or braces with a full floral skirt. Wear a bow tie in your hair. The unexpected accessory is straight from Pandora's Box. Keep your ideas flexible and have some fun.

6

IDEAS ON

IMAGE

Since we all live multi-faceted lives, the clothes which we buy must be versatile, must suit all aspects of our diverse interests, must be comfortable and, above all, must project the desired image. In fact, there is usually a considerable discrepancy between the message that our clothes give out and what we really are, since much of the time we dress to impress, to confuse and to deceive. The trick is to recognize your own personality traits and then adapt your clothes so that you can still feel confident within the sphere of that message.

As an example, if you work in an office and are up for a promotion you will want to give off a smart, efficient air. A tailored suit and formal shirt will signal a businesslike approach and suggest you are someone who is strong, sharp, aggressive, decisive, urban, sophisticated and in control. In fact, you may be all those things, but actually prefer to dress in softer, unstructured clothes. However, the message that comes across from flowing casuals, particularly if they are in pastel shades, patterned, have frills and bows or are made from soft fabrics like suede, is a friendly, caring, gentle, relaxed, innocent or passive person – in fact, the sort of qualities that don't inspire confidence when a company is looking for someone to suit a tough managerial position.

If, however, you are a classic or dramatic dresser anyway, wearing this sort of clothing will be second nature to you. It is the naturals and romantics who will have to adapt, but not in such a way that it looks as if you have tried too hard. If you look 'too' anything, the effect will rebound against you. The options are these. Since a suit is associated with executive status, choose one that is tailored but made from a soft fabric like flannel or tweed. Make sure that it has rounded shoulderpads, not hard square ones. Choose a jacket style that has some curved seaming, curved lapels or some slight gathering at the sleevehead. The skirt, too, need not be straight, but could have some gathers at the waistband or a front pleat – and, of course, it must be a basic colour from the range that suits your skin tones. In this way, you can get across the right message but in a format that won't fight your personality.

First Impressions

During the first few moments of meeting someone your appearance will be giving clues to your personality. Hairstyles, make-up and clothes are all symbols which you can bring into play either consciously or subconsciously. Which message you want to put across will depend on your situation. The day messages are often restricted by a conventional job or a desire to blend in with the surroundings and conform to 'normal', dressing, that is, clothes which don't stand out or attract attention. Night messages, however, could give conflicting information if, for example, you wanted to let your hair down and indulge in wearing some outrageous jewellery, a tight dress in a bright colour or a flashy fabric. The message suggests you are sexy, fun, extrovert and exciting. Blatant messages are generally treated with suspicion, whereas subtle ones are more intriguing. Simply taking note of what people are 'saying' with their clothes can help you to evaluate their personality and in some instances can turn a situation to your advantage. At a job interview, for instance, here are three typical messages:

Conventional Keep appearance neat, well-groomed, clean, sensible and sober by wearing discreet make-up and jewellery, an unfussy hairstyle, a high-necked blouse, a knee-length skirt, flesh-coloured tights and low-heeled shoes. By wearing traditional, classic clothes, the message suggests you are respectable, reliable, steadfast and honest.

Trendy Wearing a collection of fashionable clothes suggests the message that you are not stuck in a rut, you are progressive and that you are going places.

Individualist An innovator rather than a follower of fashion trends, your appearance will be distinctive and unconventional. Clothes and accessories look off-beat, using unusual combinations. The message suggests you are special, unique and creative.

Dressing the Part

If three women were each presented with the same jacket and skirt and a variety of tops and accessories, three very different looks would emerge. Age, personality and fashion consciousness would all play a part in the final choice of outfit, each woman expressing her own ideas of how she would like to look. Sometimes it's possible for this image to become fixed, to be so predictable as to become boring. As you get older it's natural that you should find a way of dressing that pleases you and fits into your lifestyle, but it is also easy to get into a rut. Experimenting with different colour and clothes combinations, changing the accessories and keeping an eye on the trends is an easy way of putting some fashion zip back into your appearance.

Versatile Separates

Here are three different images to show how clothes can change your age:

1. Young and casual Take one jacket and one basic skirt. Add a chambray shirt, tartan earrings, tartan bow tie, a casual belt, a fun watch, a satchel bag, ribbed tights and casual loafers.

2. Older and smarter Take one jacket and one basic skirt. Add a pale, fine cotton blouse with a pretty neckline, gilt earrings, smart leather belt, gilt chain bracelet, neat shoulder bag, dark flesh tights, low-heeled leather pumps.

3. Oldest and sophisticated Take one jacket and one basic skirt. Add one dark top, pearl necklace and earrings, a silky cummerbund and pocket hanky, a smart watch, sheer dark tights, clutch bag and patent court shoes.

Ringing the changes with clever use of accessories

Imagine the Image

Half the fun of fashion is changing your image according to your fancy; the same city slicker clothes can convert into casuals or evening wear by just switching things around. Borrowing ideas from history or even from your husband helps make your wardrobe more versatile, but most of the time it is your accessories that give the impression of what you are trying to convey. The basic clothes stay the same and can be worn in innumerable different ways.

Man appeal Take one pair of classic trousers, one jacket, one pin-striped shirt. Add a bow tie or a conventional tie, preferably striped or spotted, a pocket handkerchief, a pair of cuff links and a man's watch, braces, a plain leather belt and sensible lace-up shoes.

Just dandy Take one pair of classic trousers, one jacket, one pin-striped shirt. Add a lace cravat at the neck, a stick pin, a brocade waistcoat, a fob watch, leather gloves and button boots.

Just casual Take one pair of classic trousers, one jacket, one pin-striped shirt, opened at the neck. Add one diamond-patterned pullover and matching socks, loafers, a chunky leather belt, gold earrings and bracelet watch.

Style Seekers

When nothing in the high street shops appeals to you, try looking for inspiration elsewhere. The humble jumble sale can throw up unexpected delights and sometimes real bargains. Charity shops are a good source of men's jackets, ties and belts, as well as knitwear and blouses; dress agencies specialize in the nearly new and usually have a good selection of party or special occasion clothes. Antique shops and auctions are well aware that lace-collared blouses and Victorian nightgowns are in great demand for pretty summer clothes, so consequently the bargains are harder to find. Period clothes still represent a unique style, however, and in terms of workmanship are real value for money.

By injecting fresh ideas into your wardrobe and adapting different images, mixing together different textures, patterns and colour, the permutations of your clothes will be limitless. Provided you understand your personality, colouring and figure type you will know how to be smart without being stuffy; how to be feminine without being frilly; how to be casual without being scruffy; how to be witty without being way-out; how to be fashionable without feeling foolish; how to be exciting without being extreme. All you need is some time to experiment with your looks and I promise it will be time well spent.

Section two

Beauty Focus

7

COMMONSENSE

SKIN CARE

A clear, glowing complexion is an outward sign that all is well with our health and, although we are mainly concerned with how it looks and feels, this complex organ is a vital part of our whole system and is intricately linked with the total body chemistry. Skin acts like a barometer and can be affected by age, diet, the elements, the nervous system, medication and emotions so, since it is a living organism with changing reactions and moods, keep your ideas flexible when it comes to looking after it. And it certainly is worth looking after, because not only will constant care pay dividends later in life, but smooth skin will enhance make-up and, together with shiny hair, create an instant favourable impact.

Skin works around the clock, shedding impurities, replacing old skin with new, supplying natural oils through the sebaceous glands and providing its own delicate outer film of sebum, which protects the skin against excessive moisture or dehydration and the effects of extreme weather conditions and pollution. The suppleness and bloom of the skin is largely dependent on its moisture content, which is why, since the skin varies in thickness, a thinly-stretched patch such as the eyelid area is prone to drying up and wrinkling and is one of the first places to show signs of ageing.

The replenishment and moisture-retaining quality of the skin cells, then, is of great importance. Each cell has a life cycle of around 21–28 days and is formed in the basal layer of the epidermis, or outer layer of skin. These cells push upwards to the surface where, no longer living, they flake off as a result of washing or rubbing. They are easily visible when your skin is particularly dry because it develops a patchy, flaky appearance caused by these clusters of dead skin cells.

The middle layer of skin, known as the dermis, is made up of a variety of fibres which give the skin its strength and elasticity. It also contains hair follicles, the glands that produce sebum and sweat, nerve endings and the blood vessels, which give the skin some of its colour as well as delivering nutrients and vitamins and helping to eliminate waste matter. All these are set in a solid mass of connective tissue, most of which is a protein substance called collagen.

Beneath this is the deepest layer of skin, the subcutaneous tissue, consisting mainly of fat cells and blood vessels which act as a cushion against injury, a heat insulator and a storage area for nutrients.

Most of the action takes place in the dermis, and it is here that the skin's own supply of oil begins the journey to the surface pores. Some places are more prone to oil spillage than others – the scalp, face, mid-chest and shoulder blades

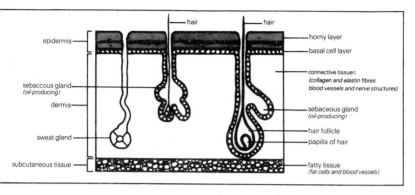

epidermis
horny layer
basal cell layer

hair   hair

sebaccous gland
(oil-producing)

dermis

sweat gland

subcutaneous tissue

connective tissues
(collagen and elastin fibres
blood vessels and nerve structures)

sebaceous gland
(oil-producing)

hair follicle

papilla of hair

fatty tissue
(fat cells and blood vessels)

are common gathering points. Sweat and sebum together form a thin film known as the skin's acid mantle which, apart from keeping the skin soft and supple, helps protect it against infection. The degree of activity of the sweat and sebum glands helps determine your skin type, and in order to choose the right products to cleanse and moisturize your skin it helps to identify the various skin conditions.

How to Recognize Different Skin Types

Most skins fall into one of four different types. Many people, however, have what is known as a combination skin, which usually consists of an oily panel down the centre of the face with the surrounding areas being dry. If, when you have considered the four types below, you decide you have a combination skin, treat each area separately, using the routines for dry and oily skin as appropriate.

Sensitive Skin

Characteristics Skin sensitivity and allergic reactions can be triggered off by pollution, humidity, dust, stress, chemicals in products in daily use, change of diet or illness. Two kinds of substances harm the skin: irritants, which damage the skin cells on contact, and sensitizers, which have a cumulative effect and cause an inflammation after repeated usage. Allergy symptoms are redness, swelling, heat and pain. Milder reactions cause itching and stinging. Sensitive skin symptoms are florid colouring, blotchy red marks, easy flushing, dryness, flakiness, distended veins and easy aggravation by sun and wind.

Treatment Use specialist skin products containing no perfume, colouring or additives that could cause problems. Try to buy trial or small sizes at first to test for reactions. Remember that 'natural' ingredients such as sunflower or cucumber could be just as lethal as a man-made ingredient. Use only hypo-allergenic make-up.

Avoid All highly-perfumed products, strong sun and dry atmospheres.

Dry Skin

Characteristics Dry skin is generally fine-textured, with a taut appearance and, often, fine lines around the eyes and mouth. It lacks tone and freshness and tends to flake or become rough. Make-up sits on the skin and looks patchy.
Treatment In the morning use a rich cleansing cream folllowed by a creamy skin freshener without a drying alcohol content. Use moisturizer under make-up along with an oil-based cream or liquid foundation and cream eye shadows and blushers. Use powder sparingly. In the evening, cleanse and tone as before and follow up with a rich moisture cream and a light eye cream applied very gently around the eyes. Always remove the surplus with damp cotton wool, since an overdose of moisture can result in puffy eyes.
Avoid Normal toilet soaps, which are slightly alkaline and make a dry skin feel 'tight' after usage. Avoid extremes of temperature, drastic dieting and excess alcohol.

Oily Skin

Characteristics An oily skin has an obvious shine, even through make-up and soon after washing it exudes oil and moisture and is frequently troubled with blackheads and blemishes. Enlarged pores or a coarse-texture are common and the skin is prone to look sallow.
Treatment Thorough cleansing is especially important. Use specially formulated cleansing bars with a complexion brush to loosen oil-plugged pores. Rinse thoroughly and apply an astringent, followed by a light moisturizer. Make-up should be an all-in-one matt foundation smoothed on with a damp sponge, but for a really difficult skin try a medicated make-up. Remove make-up using a cleansing lotion, not cream, followed by an astringent. For bad spots, spread tissue over the spotty area after cleansing and dab each spot through the tissue with a cotton bud dipped in saline solution (one heaped teaspoon of salt dissolved in warm water). Leave on while you sleep and remove with morning cleansing. Never squeeze spots or blackheads – it breaks the skin, which can then become infected. Once a week give your face a steam bath (bend your head over a steaming bowl of water, drape a towel over your head and the bowl and remain for about fifteen minutes). Follow this with an astringent face mask to tighten the pores. Once a month use an exfoliating product to help clear skin debris. These come as gels, lotions or creams and contain micro-

scopic granules to help lift away dead surface cells and to stimulate the skin circulation.

Avoid All heavy creams, super-fatted soap and all oily, fatty foods such as chips, cream cakes and chocolate. Drink plenty of water with added lemon juice.

Normal Skin

Characteristics Fine pores around the nose and a general bloom with a smooth, fine texture. The skin will be a good colour and not unduly sensitive.

Treatment Cleanse with lotion or cream or use a soluble cream-with-water preparation. Follow up with a mild skin freshener and a light moisturizer. Use a translucent tinted moisturizer to show off youthful skin or finish off with a more covering liquid foundation. At night, cleanse and tone as before and use a cream or lotion to moisturize and a light eye cream. A weekly face mask keeps pores taut. Mix your own with some fruity ingredients – mashed peaches or apricots with a few drops of olive oil and light moisturizing cream. Leave on for fifteen minutes, rinse thoroughly with lukewarm water and finish with a moisturizer.

Avoid The temptation to nibble between-meal snacks. Stick to a balanced diet with plenty of exercise and remember that inner beauty radiates through your skin, so avoid late nights and tense situations.

Skin Care Routine

A simple but regular morning and evening skin care routine is the realistic approach to improving your skin from the outside.

Cleansing

This effectively gets rid of dirt and bacteria that have accumulated on the surface, along with the dead skin cells that need to be removed to prevent the skin from looking dingy. Wearing make-up necessitates an even more stringent cleansing routine to remove the oil-based or wax-based preparations. Cleansing milks, creams and lotions help to loosen the dirt, which must then be wiped away with damp cotton wool (or rinsed off with water if you prefer to use the specially formulated creams designed to emulate the actions of soap and water).

What you use on your skin will depend on your own preferences and on your skin type, but one of the best ways to ensure that the skin is really clean is to remove make-up with a cream cleanser and then wash your face with a complexion soap. If your skin is dry, choose a super-fatted soap containing a high percentage of oils. If your skin is oily, choose a clear glycerine soap. Afterwards, make sure you rinse thoroughly with lots of tepid water. If you use water that is too hot or too cold it will cause damage to the tiny blood vessels and result in broken veins and redness.

Specially formulated eye make-up remover is the perfect answer to cleaning off stubborn colour around the eyes. Impregnated pads and clear liquid removers are fine for removing non-waterproof make-up but use a thicker cream or lotion, or even Vaseline, for heavier make-up. Always treat the eye area with great gentleness and never rub, pull or stretch the delicate skin.

Freshening

Toners are used to remove the last traces of cleansers and skin debris and to make the skin feel fresh. Depending on the formula, toners can be alcohol-based astringents which are good for oily skins and help remove excess sebum from the surface of the skin, or milder, alcohol-free lotions. These formulations, often based on lavender water or rose water, are excellent for dry skin types.

Moisturizing

Women with dry skins are prone to wrinkles unless moisturizers are used from an early age. Oily skins secrete more natural oils, so are in less danger. However, all skins benefit from moisturizer, not because you can add moisture to your cells but because you can protect your skin from losing what is already there. Water from your body is drawn up from within the dermis and helps to keep the skin's surface cells moist, plumped-up and firm. All these cells are partially waterproofed by natural oils, but in adverse conditions such as a dry, windy atmosphere, extreme cold or long exposure to water the natural lipids become vulnerable and are not sufficient protection – hence the importance of added lubrication.

Moisturizers have two functions: they form an occlusive (i.e. moisture-proof) barrier that helps prevent dehydration and they supply the surface layer of skin with extra moisture (water is an important ingredient in most moisturizers), some of which gradually penetrates the cell walls, attracted by the fluids within the basal layers of the skin. Inevitably, much of the surface water content of a light moisturizer simply evaporates, but it does leave on the skin a thin film of oil which helps prevent moisture loss. Water-in-oil (oil-based) emulsions are generally richer than oil-in-water preparations and are therefore more suited to dry skins. Oil-in-water (water-based) emulsions are more fluid in content and are best suited to oily skins.

Since, by its very nature, skin is difficult to penetrate from the outside, many of the nourishing creams which claim to feed the skin with special nutrients, proteins, vitamins or elastin or collagen derivatives are probably not getting deep enough to do much good. They will still be moisturizing the skin, however, so they don't do any harm, either. It is the internal blood supply that is the important factor in skin nourishment and this is why you are what you eat!

Skin and Diet

Skin really does reflect what you eat, so if your food is rich in nutrients your skin will look clear and have a natural luminosity. A diet that is high in fresh fruit, vegetables, salad stuffs, wholegrain cereals, some protein and fatty acids and plenty of fibre-rich foods will benefit your skin as well as your general health.

High-fibre foods (grains, vegetables, fruit) together with plenty of water (preferably mineral, because it contains no chemicals) will aid the kidneys to flush out toxins and help to eliminate waste products speedily from the body – if food lingers too long in the system the wastes start to be absorbed back into the bloodstream.

Fish, poultry and vegetable protein are good for building healthy cells, while cereals, fruit, vegetables and low-fat dairy foods will provide essential vitamins and minerals. Vitamin A is particularly good for combating dry skin (good sources are carrots, spinach, watercress, parsley, peppers, apricots, eggs, skimmed milk and fish oils) and so is Vitamin E (green vegetables, wheatgerm, eggs, sunflower and saf-flower oils). The B-complex vitamins are also vital for combating skin problems and ensuring good circulation; they are found in wholegrains, liver, brewer's yeast, beans and pulses and wholewheat bread. Vitamin C is essential for strong, elastic skin structure and can be found in citrus fruits, berry fruits, green vegetables, tomatoes and bean sprouts.

Skin and Temperament

A calm approach to life may be the answer to good skin. Tension and emotional upsets interfere with digestion, so food is sometimes only partially broken down and nutrients are not released for absorption. Try to unwind before sitting down to a meal and take your time over your food. If you are prone to indigestion avoid drinking water just before and during a meal as it dilutes the digestive enzymes. Work off nervous energy, anger or frustration by doing some hard exercise before a meal. Apart from pepping up your circulation, it may help to get rid of some adrenalin. This hormone slows up the skin's cell-building process when it floods our bodies in huge quantities if we are agitated or excited, and the adrenal gland only stops production when we are asleep – a good argument for keeping calm and getting a reasonable quota of sleep on a regular basis.

Skin and the Elements

The English rose complexion is famous all over the world and we have our damp weather to thank for that. Skin is able to draw moisture from the damp air and humid conditions, whereas hot, dry air attracts the moisture out of the skin. In ideal conditions the cell moisture would stay put, but that rarely happens since skin has a love/hate relationship with water. Soaking the hands in water, for instance, interferes with the skin's natural lipids because they are slightly soluble. They get sluiced away by water, dissolved by detergent, partially removed by soap, frisked away by brisk towelling and evaporated by cold air on wet skin. For a while the body's own moisturizing system will break down, but you can help to allow the body to take in moisture slowly by keeping your body fluids topped up and encourage the moisture to stay in the cells by keeping your skin well oiled and protected, especially during the summer and winter months.

Winter Skin Care

Poor circulation is at the root of many winter complaints. Cold feet and hands, dull skin and cellulite are all linked to a sluggish blood flow. Healthy skin glows when blood flows freely through the tiny capillaries near the surface but when the skin is cold these vessels contract to retain heat loss, resulting in pale, pallid skin. Further attempts by the body to conserve heat mean that blood is drawn away from extremities like hands and feet to protect vital inner organs. Tip the balance in your favour with some action!

● Vigorous exercise is one of the best ways to generate heat in the body and redirect blood back to the skin's surface and the extremities. Stamping your feet, running on the spot, swinging your arms back and forth and clenching and unclenching your fists is not such a bad idea when waiting for a bus!

● Motivate yourself to take regular exercise by joining a club – running, squash, swimming, dancing – anything that inspires you to move!

● Use a massage mitt while you are having your shower or bath to stimulate circulation and then rub in your favourite body cream.

● Stimulate facial circulation by briskly tapping the face all over with the tips of your fingers, starting with your chin and moving upwards to the forehead. Then smooth the skin with moisturizers, following the diagram overleaf. Finally, pull faces at yourself – smile broadly, raise your eyebrows, blow your cheeks in and out, bite the air. Strange as this sounds it helps to tighten up facial muscles.

● Watch out for the effects of central heating, bitter winds and icy cold weather. All three will draw out the moisture from the skin and can lead to excessive dehydration. Keep your moisturizer handy and use it to balance and protect your skin.

● Chapped lips are due to moisture evaporating – fast. Unlike other skin surfaces, the lips do not conceal any sebaceous oil glands so they are very vulnerable in cold, windy weather. Protect them by using lip salves or a slick of Vaseline.

● Use blusher as a morale booster. A dash of colour around the cheeks and temples will make you look warmer.

● Grow your hair longer. It'll keep your ears warm and act as double-glazing for your scalp. Even better, get ahead, get a hat. Make it wool rather than acrylic because man-made fibres often encourage static.

● Warm wraps and gloves are beat-the-cold essentials, but nails are still prone to flakes and breaks. Give them a once-weekly treat by dipping them in a saucer of warm olive oil for ten minutes.

● Keep out the face invaders by keeping the skin soft and smooth. Before you go to bed each night, give yourself a facial massage. It's the best way to apply your moisturizing cream.

Summer Skin Care

An overdose of sunshine on the skin can cause immense damage, but a moderate amount falling on well-protected skin boosts confidence, intensifies the colour of your eyes and makes your teeth look whiter. Even better, the very act of sun worship will step up the production of endorphins in the body – they are the natural opiates which make us feel happy and full of wellbeing. We can also relax knowing that the sunlight is busy formulating Vitamin D in our skin – essential for growth and strong bones.

Banning the Burn

Despite all the wordy warnings and the technological advances which make tanning easier and safer, carelessness in the sun, causing lobster bodies and burnt skin, still remains a problem. The reason for the inflammation is the potentially harmful ultraviolet radiation – UVA and UVB

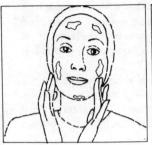 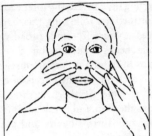 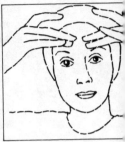

1. Begin with a clean face and smooth a moisturizing cream on the forehead, cheeks, chin and neck.

2. Massage up the sides of the nose with your second and third fingertips and, with a continuous movement, out across your forehead and temples.

3. Stay relaxed and repeat these movements several times. Keep them firm but gentle as too much pressure drags the skin.

4. Massage around the eyes by running your third fingertip from the nose under the browbone, in a circle round and

• • • • •

rays. Only five to ten per cent of the sun's rays are deeply absorbed into the skin, but the endangered cells are the very ones which give the skin its suppleness, elasticity and firmness. Warning signs that these are under attack include reddening and itching, progressing to pain, swelling and blistering and accompanying nausea and headaches. With very severe sunburn the skin's sweating mechanism could also be affected, resulting in heatstroke. Usually it takes six to eight hours after sun exposure for burning to make its presence felt, and it could get progressively worse for forty-eight hours afterwards. Ironically, this is the same period it takes for a normal tan to develop, providing you've been sensible!

Protection Racket

Naturally, when it comes to beating the burn, the name of the game is protection and the magic ingredient is called melanin. It's a dark pigment present in and around the growing layer of skin and it is the skin's own natural defence system, screening out harmful rays and providing a form of protection that we recognize as a tan. However, melanin takes time to develop, especially in areas of the body which are usually unexposed, so abused bodies are generally those that spend too long, too soon, in the sun.

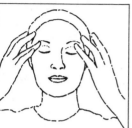  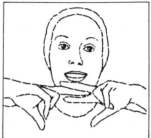

lightly underneath the eye, then back to the nose.

5. Now your neck. Using alternating hands, smooth cream downwards with your palms, stroking it under the chin and over the throat.

6. Massage the chin, using a horizontal scissor movement with the first and second fingers of your left hand and the middle finger of your right hand.

7. Finish by carefully patting away excess face cream with cotton wool pads dampened with water or skin freshener.

•   •   •   •   •

Safety in Numbers

How long you can stay in the sun without burning and without any protection at all depends entirely on your skin type and the strength of the sun. When you choose suntan preparations, look for the sun protection factor number on the packet. The SPF simply means it has built-in protective qualities, graded according to strength. The higher the number on the pack, the more protection you will get. The fairer your skin is, the higher the number you'll need. An SPF of six, for instance, gives a fair-skinned person about an hour of trouble-free tanning – six times longer than the ten minutes she would normally be able to survive without any protective cream. Olive-complexioned people, however, usually contain more natural oil in their skins, so can afford to stay in the sun slightly longer and perhaps start off with a lower SPF.

Face Savers

Your face, more than any other part of your body, is so vulnerable that it deserves special attention. Products especially formulated for the prevention of dryness and the protection of delicate areas such as around the eyes, the tops of the cheekbones, the nose and the lips are worthwhile investments and often come in a convenient solid stick form.

For larger areas, such as tops of the shoulders and feet and the breast bone, use high protection creams or a sun block product.

Be Prepared

Smooth, supple skin is easier to lubricate, soaks up the sun and holds a tan longer, so it pays to prepare your skin before, as well as during the holidays. Many of the specialist pre-tan lotions which are meant to be used in advance of the holiday claim to stimulate the melanin production in the skin and therefore do more than just act as a body lotion. However, a jumbo-sized pack of the latter is an investment for moisture-deprived skin and is often less expensive than an after-sun product which basically does the same job. After your sun ration, shower away all the sun lotion, perspiration, sand and salt and apply a liberal dollop of body lotion or cooling lubrication which will help prolong your tan for the days when the sunshine is just a distant memory. Without doubt, a bit of forward planning can alleviate all the potential problems of sudden exposure, provided you treat the sun's rays with respect and use products especially designed to protect your skin from sun damage.

Ten Tips For Sun Safety

● In a sunny climate, your skin deserves a holiday too. A gradual build-up of colour is kinder to your skin and will last longer. If you rush out on the first day of your holiday covered in oil and sizzle till sunset you are asking for trouble. Short bursts of sun are always better and safer than lengthy sunning sessions.

● Only mad dogs and Englishmen go out in the midday sun, so stay sane and avoid the noonday heat. Sunlight is at peak power between eleven and three o'clock, since the higher the sun moves in the sky the less ozone layers there are for the rays to penetrate en route to earth. Settle for a siesta instead of sunburn.

● Don't let hazy days fool you. Even when you move into the shade, indirect sunlight can be scattered by molecules in the atmosphere and can still do plenty of damage. Never underestimate the power of the sun.

● Face up to the sun with sunglasses. Dazzle and glare from the sun can cause headaches, so reduce ultraviolet light penetration by investing in the best pair of specs you can afford. Good quality plastic or glass lenses should not distort your vision and should always feel comfortable.

● Take extra care when sunbathing near reflective surfaces such as sand, concrete or white walls. The sun's rays bounce back and burn much faster. Don't fall into the suntrap of lazing without lubrication!

● Become water-wise. Sea and pool water transmit a good proportion of the sun's rays, so don't spend hours on a lilo or alternate between swimming and sunbathing without constant renewal of sun lotion. Children, as well as adult water babies, will benefit from special waterproof sunscreening products ideal for splashing about in the waves.

● **Play safe and apply your sun-screen before you venture out into the heat. You could burn up just walking to the beach, for it only takes about thirteen minutes exposure in the scorching Mediterranean sun to cook the average Brit!**

● Beware of the cooling breeze, especially on boat journeys or driving around in open-topped cars. It's easy to forget how hot the sun really is and even clothes don't always give full protection – a wet T-shirt, for instance, will let through some ultraviolet rays. Cover up with tight weave, rather than loose weave, natural fabrics such as cotton for maximum protection.

● **Be aware that some chemicals, perfumes or drugs such as the contraceptive pill, antibiotics, diuretics or tranquillizers could spark off a reaction in your skin that will be aggravated by the sun. The skin may appear blotchy, tanning unevenly, in which case check with your doctor. As a precaution, if you think your skin is susceptible stick with unperfumed suntan products and don't wear perfume.**

● The best way to get an all-over, even tan is to keep active. Walk along the beach, play beach games, or take up water sports. Remember to reapply lotion at regular intervals, especially if you've been sweating or using a towel to wipe yourself down. You'll tan more quickly and keep fit, all at the same time!

Skin Enemies

Apart from the elements and environmental pollution, there are other influences that affect the skin.

Smoking Smoking can age your skin and make it look distinctly jaded. When you smoke, the nicotine in the cigarette constricts tiny blood vessels in your skin, preventing blood being freely circulated and interfering with the natural waste disposal system. Efficient blood supply is vital for clear skin, so smokers may suffer from blocked pores, premature wrinkling and a pallid skin.

Alcohol An excess of alcohol is one fluid you can do without, since it disturbs the body's natural fluid balance, causes the blood vessels to dilate so that cells become oxygen-starved and in some cases results in broken veins and a florid complexion. It also interferes with the efficient functioning of your liver, with consequent hormone imbalances.

Toxins Even tea and coffee, which contain the drug caffeine, can do long term damage by stimulating the nervous system and bringing about physiological changes. Avoid these toxins by drinking plenty of alternative liquids such as mineral water and herbal teas.

Hormone Upsets Hormones are complex chemical messengers found in the bloodstream and are part of a delicately balanced network which cannot be consciously controlled and which contributes to a wide variety of essential processes within the body. Hormone imbalances can affect your skin and this is most noticeable at puberty, when over-stimulated glands produce teenage spots and acne, or during your menstrual cycle, when skin is prone to spots immediately before and during a period. The contraceptive pill, which is the most widely used drug, artificially steps up the oestrogen (female hormone) supply, which often results in an improved, fine-textured skin and contributes towards a drier skin as we get older. During pregnancy, your skin changes again and becomes radiantly clear as natural hormonal changes begin to take place.

Common Problems

Wrinkles An inevitable result of the passage of time, they can be delayed by the use of moisturizers from an early age.

Lines on the upper lip Usually the result of dry skin, smoking, ill-fitting dentures and tension. Learn to relax your mouth, don't purse your lips and use plenty of moisturizer.

The odd spot A blocked pore is usually the problem. The best policy is to leave it to clear itself or dab with salty water to aid the drying out process. As the inflammation subsides, new, healthy cells will replace the trouble spot. If you are troubled by constant spots, check that you are receiving adequate vitamins and minerals in your diet as a deficiency may be the cause.

Blackheads Oily skins are at most risk from congestion of sebum and waste matter blocking a hair follicle. This blackens, not from grime, but from oxidization when it is exposed to air. It is possible to remove blackheads once the central core rises above the surface of the skin. Steam your face for ten minutes over a bowl of hot water then, with your fingers wrapped in cotton wool, put gentle pressure either side of the blackhead and ease it out. Alternatively, use a special blackhead extractor available from chemists. Dab with a mild antiseptic and leave the skin free from cosmetics for several hours. Thorough cleansing, regular exfoliation and a weekly face mask will help prevent blackheads.

Whiteheads These raised bumps of trapped oil lie under the surface of the skin and are often associated with an acid skin, weight problems or poor cleansing. They can be removed by a beauty therapist but will eventually disappear if dabbed with a mild medicated lotion.

Open pores Greasy skins often have an orange-peel texture where the openings for the oil secretions have been stretched by a constant and heavy oil flow. This can be helped by constant cleansing and toning, steaming, exfoliating and face packs. Go gently, though – greasy skins are not necessarily tough skins.

Broken veins These are often hereditary, but can be aggravated by poor circulation, temperature extremes, poor diet and smoking. Sensitive, delicate skins are prone to broken veins and need very gentle handling. Make-up can camouflage uneven colouring, but they can also be dispersed by professional treatment.

Discoloured skin Brown pigmentation spots can occur at any age and can be triggered by the contraceptive pill, hormonal changes or too much sun. Special creams will inhibit the production of further pigmentation in the skin cells after an elapse of some weeks, but professional peeling by the experts is one method of removal. Otherwise, use a good camouflage make-up.

Growing Older Gracefully

Throughout the various stages of life your skin will reflect the major changes, be they puberty, pregnancy or menopause, and slowly and inevitably age will take its toll. Circulation and cell renewal processes become slower, sebaceous glands provide less oil to lubricate and soften the skin, the connective tissue in the dermis begins to lose some of its elastic qualities and skin is thinner and no longer firm to the touch. The whole process happens very slowly and there are usually no real signs until around the thirties. After that, genetics become the big deciding factor of how fast we age, though sun, harsh climate, stress, diet, lifestyle, smoking or pure neglect can all contribute to ageing. Some people become more attractive with maturity, as age adds character to a face, but although you can't fight it, you can at least prevent premature ageing by looking after your looks, living a healthy lifestyle and by not giving in to lethargy about your appearance.

Age Analysis

Twenty to thirty The skin should be at its best, with teenage spots shed along with the puppy fat. However, think ahead and find time for a regular beauty regime. Thorough cleansing and moisturizing is a must and will pay dividends in later years. The skin should be smooth and supple and, since this is a very socially active time of life, be aware that you can help to keep it this way by avoiding excessive amounts of rich foods and alcohol.

Thirty to forty Positive action is needed as your skin becomes drier. Re-assess your moisturizer. Is it rich enough? Pay particular attention to your neck and eye area and make use of face masks to stimulate cell turnover.

Forty to fifty By the mid-forties, expression lines will begin to deepen around the mouth, eyes and on the forehead. The skin shows signs of loss of elasticity, especially around the eyes, and shadows become more pronounced. Facials, to help deep cleanse the skin and keep it well moisturized, are essential now, plus facial exercises to stave off any hint of a double chin.

Fifty to sixty By the mid-fifties, the skin becomes looser and the folds and sagging tissues around the eyes will be more pronounced due to loss of muscle tone. The cheeks and jaw become flabby and the nose and chin usually appear to be more prominent. Exercises to help firm the face and increase circulation will help, plus specially developed moisture creams which help the cell renewal process.

Sixty plus As we age, the skull may remain the same or start to shrink while the skin continues to grow, causing more pronounced sagging of skin and underlying muscles. Around the cheeks, delicate criss-cross wrinkles appear and also lines around the mouth deepen. The skin tone may lighten due to diminishing blood supply and loss of blood vessels, so a hint of added colour with a cream blusher may be required, plus a tinted moisturizer.

Secrets of Youthful Skin

● Exposure to the sun makes the skin tougher and more wrinkled, so don't sunbathe without protective creams and the older you get, the less time you should spend in the sun. Choose skin products with a built-in sun-screen.

● Give up smoking, not just for health reasons but because heavy smokers age faster and wrinkle earlier than non-smokers.

● The older you get the drier your skin becomes, so choosing the right cleanser and moisturizer is essential. Keep your ideas flexible and go with what feels right for your skin.

● Handle your skin as you would a piece of delicate silk chiffon. Use gentle upward and outward movements when applying creams and cleansers. Pulling, stretching and rubbing can damage the skin.

● Apply a moisturizer to a clean, warm and slightly damp skin for maximum results and to help slow down moisture loss.

● Select a light moisturizer for daytime and for use under make-up and a richer cream at night.

● Get plenty of rest, because while you sleep tense facial muscles relax and your skin cells have a chance to regenerate.

● If you keep your everyday skin care routine simple you are more likely to stick to it, but once a week boost the bloom and allow yourself time for a skin treat. Make yourself a face mask and relax for ten minutes.

● Fresh air and regular exercise keep circulation moving and pep up the vital blood supplies feeding nutrients to your skin.

● A glowing skin starts from the inside, so eat a balanced diet which includes plenty of roughage, fresh fruit and vegetables. Vitamin and mineral supplements can certainly do no harm and probably do a lot of good.

● Drink as much pure water as you can (not coffee, tea or Coca Cola, which contain diuretic caffeine) to help flush the body of toxins which otherwise may be expelled as blemishes.

● Central heating and strong cold winds extract moisture from your skin so always protect and moisturize it against temperature extremes.

● Protection and care needn't be expensive. Vaseline makes an excellent lip salve and creams without fancy packaging and massive advertising campaigns are likely to do just the same job of soothing and smoothing.

● When you know that a product suits your skin (buy a trial size first, if possible) buy the biggest size available for the most economical method of regular care. Chemists often sell simple, unbranded no-frill creams like Emulsifying Cream B.P., an inexpensive water-soluble cleanser in a jumbo jar.

● If your skin is at all sensitive, always choose unperfumed products.

● If you have any skin problems that are not clearing up, ask your GP to recommend a dermatologist.

● Dampened cotton wool pads are softer, and therefore kinder to the skin, than tissues for removing the last traces of cleanser. Tissues are fine for blotting away excess oil.

● Emotional upsets and stress take a toll on the skin, so learn to take deep breaths slowly and deeply from your diaphragm. Enlist for a yoga course.

● Whenever you touch your skin make sure your fingers are clean. Although skin is programmed to resist bacteria, these defences sometimes break down as you get older.

● If you go for a professional facial, learn all you can from the qualified practitioner. Ask questions about what she is doing and why. She should be able to confirm which skin type you have and may suggest ways of improving your skin, but resist heavy sales pressure to purchase salon products (usually expensive) unless you notice a marked improvement over the products you normally use.

● Battery operated machines which claim to tone up circulation are really a gimmick. They work, but so do your fingers. A daily facial massage when applying moisturizer is a most effective fingertip toner at no extra cost.

● Apply a body lotion after every bath or shower and make sure the water is not so hot that it dehydrates the outer layers of the skin.

● Avoid harsh alkaline soaps and always rinse well to ensure that there is no drying, irritating residue left behind. If you live in an area with 'hard' water, a teaspoon of borax, mixed with cold water, will soften it. Not quite rainwater, but the next best thing.

● After applying your moisturizer finish with a fine spray of Evian water to seal in the moisture.

● The way to tell whether your skin is really clean is to check your pad of cotton wool after use. You may have to make two or three applications of cleanser before it becomes spotless and you can go on to tone and moisturize.

● Do remember to moisturize your neck as well as your face. Crêpey skin in the neck area is a telltale sign of ageing.

● Don't ever underestimate your skin's thirst and if you have oily skin don't confuse the question of skin oil with body moisture. An excess of oil does not imply an abundance of moisture.

● When travelling by air always carry a moisturizer with you in your handbag and replenish your skin's supply around the clock. Pressurized cabins drain the moisture from your skin.

● Take care of your eyelids because the fine skin here and around the eye area will be the first to show signs of ageing. Use a special eye make-up remover before regular cleansing. Pat a little wheatgerm oil or special eye gel into the tissues around eyes. Avoid heavy creams, which may cause morning puffiness. Use cooling pads of cucumber slices on the eyelids while resting the eyes.

● Scientific advances genuinely mean improved skin creams but, so far, no-one has produced the magic youth formula which can counter the effects of old age. Although some penetration to the outer layer of skin does occur, the essential ingredients for plumped-out smooth skin can't be greatly influenced by these emollients, although as moisturizers they are most effective. You pay your money and take your choice.

8

COMMONSENSE

HAIR CARE

Glossy hair, shaped in a style that suits your face shape, is just one more shining example of how you can make a personal statement about your appearance. Clean, healthy-looking hair helps create a good impression and, like skin, is a reflection of a healthy body.

A Head Start

Healthy hair is made up of 89 per cent protein and is a living, breathing and feeding filament which needs to be both internally nourished and externally nurtured. Unfortunately, many influences can upset or affect the natural balance of hair, from diet and hormones, weather and water to colourant chemicals and conditioners. Each head of hair will respond differently, since colour, texture, amount and shape vary from person to person.

Considering the main function of hair is to protect the underlying skin and to help maintain and regulate body temperature, such a fragile structure is deceiving. Each hair root is contained in a follicle made of epidermal cells and starts below the outer layer of the skin in a little nodule called the papilla, while the hair shaft is the visible part above the surplus of the scalp. As it nears the surface the hair gets a thin coating of sebum, or oil, from the sebaceous gland, which gives it softness and pliability. Once it reaches the surface the hair no longer receives nourishment from the papilla and is then dependent on outside help.

Each hair strand has three layers – the medulla, or middle core; the cortex (rope-like cells), which gives most of the colour, strength and elasticity; and the cuticle, which consists of overlapping scales providing a protective sheath for the hair when it emerges on the surface of the skin. It's

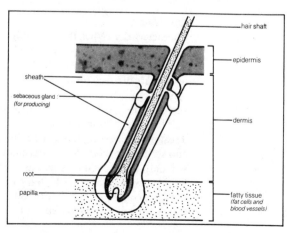

estimated that there are between 100,000–150,000 hairs on an average human head, all at varying stages of production. Each hair has its own life cycle – a long growth period, from 2–6 years, followed by a short resting period of about three months. At this stage hairs are easily dislodged by washing, brushing and combing and normal daily hair loss is anything from 50 to 150 hairs. Normally, though, new hairs form in the follicle and begin their cycle, and only when the rate of hair loss exceeds the new growth does thinning become apparent.

Age, of course, is a major contributor to hair thinning as well as to the change of colour which results in greying or white hair. Hair colour is determined by melanin, a pigment contained in the cortex layer, but as we get older, the production of pigmentation slows down. As with skin, there are ways to improve hair colour and texture designed to delay the inevitable, but good general hair care will benefit all ages. Get to know about your hair; the more you are able to do with it, the better it will affect the way you look and feel.

Hair Types

Hair varies with the individual and has different textures relative to age and race. In general, negroid races have dark, curly, sometimes frizzy hair, which is flat when seen in cross section; Orientals have coarse, strong, straight dark hair which is circular in cross section; Caucasian hair is fine, light and wavy and is oval-shaped in cross section. Everyone has both coarse and fine hair, the coarse sections usually being on the nape area while the front hairline is usually fine. Hair colour can also indicate texture type – blonde being finest, red the coarsest and brown in between. Your hair type also depends on oil activity within the skin.

Oily Hair

Characteristics When the oil glands produce more than can be comfortably absorbed the resulting hair quickly looks greasy and in need of a wash. An oily complexion and fine texture are often combined with excess oiliness and the only solution to this condition is a clean scalp. Buy a gentle shampoo designed for frequent use and wash whenever your hair looks or feels in need.

Treatment Use your shampoo sparingly and wash your hair and scalp very gently – don't scrub or over-massage as this will only stimulate the oil glands – rinsing thoroughly and finishing with cold water. If your hair is suffering from split ends, use conditioner on the dry ends only. As with oily skin, watch your diet and steer clear of animal fats, fried foods, carbohydrates, eggs, nuts, salad dressing and alcohol. Drink lots of water and introduce more roughage to your diet in the form of plenty of raw vegetables and fresh fruit. Choose a short, easily washed hairstyle and try not to wear hats or scarves. Towel dry rather than blow dry and wash brushes and combs frequently. Don't style or over-handle your hair and use a comb in preference to a brush.

Dry Hair

Characteristics In complete contrast to oily hair, this is when the oil glands produce too little lubrication and it is often associated with a dry skin. However, other factors such as harsh chemicals, over-usage of electrical appliances such as tongs and heated rollers, central heating or temperature extremes can also make the hair dry and thus, on a short term basis, can be combined with any skin type. Dry hair is usually hard to control, full of static and lacks lustre. Treating dandruff can cause dry hair since, in an attempt to cure the dandruff, the wrong shampoo is often used, preventing the natural oils from reaching the base of the hair shaft.

Treatment Wash with a specially formulated shampoo and always use a conditioner. Avoid drying conditions like saunas, sunshine or central heating. Stop frequent use of electrical appliances such as heated rollers and have your hair trimmed often to stop split ends from advancing up the shaft. A once-a-week oil treatment before shampooing will leave the hair soft and glossy. Section the hair and dab on warm olive or a light vegetable oil. As the entire scalp becomes saturated, use your fingers to massage the oil into the hair and scalp, wrap your head with cling-film and then cover with a towel. This ensures heat and moisture will work together for a lustrous result. The longer you leave the treatment on, the better it is.

Problem Hair

Characteristics Mixed conditions can cause an oily scalp with dry hair. The scalp may feel dry and be flaking with dandruff scales, but the hair shaft is actually drying out due to sebum from the follicle soaking into the dandruff flakes and clogging the flow of oil along the shaft.

Treatment Clear the scalp of flaking scales by using a mild anti-dandruff shampoo or a lotion applied after the head has been shampooed and conditioned. Once the scaling has cleared, use a shampoo for dry hair, a conditioner and then an anti-dandruff lotion to ensure that the scalp remains clear.

Normal Hair

Characteristics Shining, well-behaved hair is the crowning glory that we all strive for. Hair with the correct balance has a clear scalp, a good flow of oil and doesn't need washing too frequently. If your skin is also in good condition, you could be reaping the benefits of a healthy lifestyle, a nutritious diet, plenty of sleep and regular exercise. The latter is the perfect pep-up for hair, since it stimulates the circulation, bringing oxygen through the bloodstream to feed the hair follicles. It also relaxes the mind and muscles, easing tension and stress – one of the hair's worst enemies. However, hair won't always stay on an even keel. It may need extra treatment after a holiday in the sun, after illness or a course of medication, and particularly after a perm or a tint.

Treatment A mild shampoo, as often as necessary, followed by a conditioner and a thorough rinsing will keep it looking good. Use a hair mask or a deep conditioning treatment once a month.

Feed Your Hair

Diet is the most effective way of keeping your hair healthy, so get into good eating habits and throw out all over-refined and 'junk' foods. Stock up on proteins like lean meat for Vitamin E and liver for Vitamin A; fish for iron and Vitamin A; eggs for Vitamin B and D; tuna fish and liver for Vitamin D. Other goodies include natural yoghurt, cottage cheese, milk and small amounts of other cheeses and butter.

Cook vegetables lightly or, better still, eat them raw. Vegetables and fresh fruit are a good source of all the essential minerals and vitamins. Foods such as wholemeal bread, brown rice, potatoes in their jackets, wholewheat cereal, pasta and pulses are excellent sources of roughage.

Specific problems relating to oily hair can be helped by adjusting your diet so as to reduce fat, fatty meats (tinned and fresh), all fried foods, butter, margarine and lard.

More mature women or those with normally dry hair will see an improvement if they vary their diet to include more oily fish, unsalted nuts and seeds and peanut butter.

Come Clean

A shampoo can't alter the hair quality but it can improve the outward appearance if you choose the right product. Soapless or synthetic detergent shampoos are the most common types available. They lather easily, are non-irritant, rinse off quickly and don't normally damage the hair structure. They are made chiefly from water containing some or all of the following: chemicals, preservatives, dye for the colour, thickening, wetting and softening agents, foaming properties, conditioner, fragrance and herbal or protein extract. Major differences are usually over perfume content, cleansing and conditioning abilities or the specific hair type that they are designed to help. Shampoos will only clean a surface, so no matter what added protein or vitamins a product claims to have, it cannot be absorbed by the hair; it merely adds a protective layer and bonds damaged hair.

Shampoo Shorts

● Buy a small sachet or trial-size shampoo until you are sure that it suits you.

● Read the label carefully to see which shampoo corresponds to your hair type. The choice is confusing so you'll have to experiment.

● Judge by the results if you have it right. If your hair feels clean and looks lustrous you are on to a winner.

● Don't use too much shampoo – it won't make the hair any cleaner. As a rough guide, use two tablespoons for long hair, one for medium length and less for short hair.

● If you wash your hair very frequently you will probably need only one application. Too much shampoo will strip the hair shaft of all its own natural oils.

● Avoid bottles with large openings – you'll end up tipping out too much shampoo and that's like throwing money down the plughole.

● Change your shampoo from time to time. It prevents the scalp from building up a resistance to familiar ingredients.

● Don't make your choice of shampoo on the basis of pretty packaging, clever advertising or a pleasing perfume, and don't think that thickness equals richness, or that because a shampoo doesn't lather much it's no good.

● Never use pure detergent or washing-up liquid as soap or shampoo substitutes. Because they are strongly alkaline they interfere with the hair's natural balance, weakening the hair structure and making it more prone to breaking and splitting.

Washing Wiles

Shampooing regularly will ensure that hair is kept free of dust, grime and excess oil (and is especially necessary if you live in a city) but the most important thing to remember is that when hair is wet it is vulnerable and easily overstretched, so handle with care.

● Begin by brushing dry hair thoroughly with a pure bristle brush to help remove dust and tangles. Always tackle the latter by working from the ends to the top, thus avoiding strain on the roots. If you don't remove knots before wetting the hair it becomes matted.

● You should preferably wash your hair under a shower or hairspray attachment since this is the easiest way to control the water temperature and ensures plenty of water flow for the rinse-off.

● Make sure your hair gets a thorough wetting by keeping the spray close to your head and so enabling the water to get to the scalp. Make sure the water is not too hot or you may burn your scalp or over-activate the oil glands.

● Follow the instructions on the shampoo. If they suggest leaving the shampoo on for a certain length of time, do it!

● Using a small amount of shampoo in the palm of your hand, rub your hands together then apply liberally through the hair, first with the palms and then with the fingertips. Begin at the top of the head and work down, massaging lightly to produce lather.

● Use less shampoo if you live in a soft water area because this will cause it to lather more easily.

● Never rub, drag or pull the hair when washing it, especially the fragile ends, and be careful not to scratch the scalp with your nails.

● Pay particular attention to the hairline around the face and neck where perspiration gathers and make-up may be trapped.

Rinsing
Poor rinsing is often the cause of dull-looking hair, so spend time on this stage. Use the shower head to force jets of water through the hair to the underneath sections and stroke the water over your head from nape to the front hairline. Once all the scum and shampoo have been rinsed away the water will run clear. Pat the hair gently with a towel to remove excess moisture that may dilute the conditioner.

Conditioner   A conditioner for your hair does the same job as a moisturizer for your skin. It counteracts dryness of the hair shaft, coats the hair with a protective wax, smooths the cuticle scales and allows light to bounce off the surface to give the customary shine associated with clean, healthy hair. Conditioner is spread gently through your hair using your fingers or a wide-toothed comb. Wrap your hair in a towel and leave on for the recommended time. Finally, rinse off thoroughly. There are several types of conditioners to choose from, or you can make your own:

Conditioning rinses These are light formulations which will untangle hair and which are applied straight after shampooing. They coat the hair's surface with a thin layer of wax, oil or lanolin, reduce static and keep the hair smooth. They are good for oily hair.

Conditioners These aim to give hair extra body or restore texture and suppleness to damaged hair and are usually creams, waxes, balsams and conditioning setting lotions. Oil-free formulations are good for oily hair. They have a deeper action than rinses and are generally left on for several minutes.

Treatments and deep conditioners Essential for hair that has been over-bleached or tinted, badly permed or dried out with too much sun. Some are applied before shampooing and others are applied afterwards, but all are left on for some time for maximum benefits.

Home-made helpers Try spreading some thick and creamy mayonnaise or mashed avocado over the hair several hours before shampooing. For a rich pre-shampoo conditioner, massage in a mixture of beaten egg, 2½ tablespoons of dried milk and 1 tablespoon of wheatgerm oil and leave for at least an hour. For a final shiny rinse dilute the juice of a fresh lemon with really cold water – especially good for blondes. Brunettes may like to try a little vinegar instead.

Styling Control Setting your hair is basically another form of hair design and it means your style can be as versatile as you wish. Whether you choose to use rollers or make finger waves, weave plaits or make pin curls, use bendy foam pieces or simply scrunch-dry your hair. Once your hair has been washed a setting agent can mean the difference between success and disaster. Choose from:

Twist and Curl

Setting lotions These come in different strengths. Usually the light to normal types are fine for the average head of hair and give body, shine and manageability. Most have conditioning properties and some are designed to help with greasy hair problems.

Blow dry lotions These are ideal for light control, volume and shine and, used in conjunction with a hairdryer, give protection against the drying effect of the hot airflow.

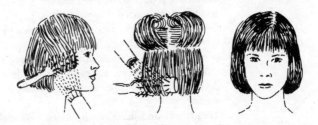

Blow dry
lotions

Gels Modern gels are non-gummy, non-stick, fast drying and help give body and volume. Many can be used on damp or dry hair and all wash out easily. Use sparingly to boost existing volume or use a heavier application for a sleek, wet, sculptured look. Gelled hair should be left alone when dry or the holding effect is lost.

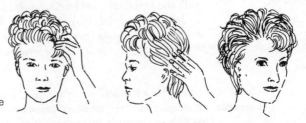

Bounce with mousse
or slick on gel

Mousse This is probably the most widely used hair aid since it adds body and bounce at the same time as holding a style with gentle firmness that lasts. Mousse can be applied to wet or dry hair. The can should be shaken well, then a small amount of mousse – about the size of a golf ball – should be squirted into the palm of your hand. Spread it quickly and evenly through your hair before drying.

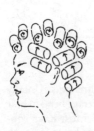

Using curlers

Using bendy foam pieces

Twist each section and as you wind the hair onto rod, twist the flexible styler around once for every complete turn. Leave for 15 minutes and comb through with fingers.

Spiral Curls Divide the hair into random sections.

Loose Curls Divide the hair into random sections. Take each section and twist the hair before winding onto the bendy rods. Leave for 15 minutes and comb through.

Extra Body Divide hair into random large sections – five down the centre and two each side – roll hair and secure the bendy rods by bending the ends. Leave for 5 minutes and brush through for instant body.

Drying In an ideal world, once the shampoo and conditioning stage is finished, after blotting wet hair with a towel the best thing would be to let it dry naturally or use your fingers to create wavy volume. But however casual the end result, the most natural styles only look good if their basis is a good cut. Hair needs shape more than ever when the finish is destined to be unstructured. However, whatever the hairstyle, most people just haven't got time to wait for nature to take its course, so need to have a little help from a hand or hood dryer. A hood dryer is generally used to speed the drying process of hair set in rollers. The hand dryer is an excellent means of whole head styling, directing the heat wherever you plan shaping or need lift. Blow drying must be done with care to avoid the hair tangling and breaking off. Here's how:

● First, test the heat temperature against your hand, keeping the highest setting for the first few minutes of general drying.

● Hold the dryer about 12 inches (30 cm) from your head and use it in short, sharp spurts.

● Keep the dryer on the move. Heat damage easily occurs from carelessness at this stage.

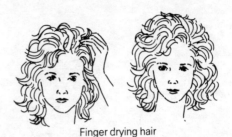

Finger drying hair

● Try to keep direct heat off the scalp and roots and exert minimal pressure on the hair with your hands.

● Divide the hair into sections, wrapping them around a brush. Large radial shapes smooth and straighten, while thin ones will curl the hair.

● As you blow above and below each section make sure the hot airstream moves with the fall of the hair, not against it.

● Start at the back of the head, working up from the nape, unfurling the hair and drying from roots to tip. Then tackle the sides and lastly dry the crown.

● Clip sections not being styled out of the way and use a waterspray to re-dampen hair that may be too dry to style.

● To give roots and a parting extra lift, raise the hair off the head at a 90° angle and dry from roots to tip.

● For general volume, angle the dryer from below or dry the hair by bending forward so that your head is upside down.

● For a feathery effect, point the dryer against the cuticle and towards the root.

● Around the hairline, blow dry hair sections in the opposite direction to which you eventually want them to lie.

● Hairspray reduces flyaway hairs and frizz. Spray a little into the palm of your hand and smooth wayward hairs into place.

● Don't overdry your hair and wait until it is cool before brushing through finally.

The Kindest Cut

The basis of a good hairstyle is a good cut, so if you never visit a hairdresser in between times at least go every two months for a trim or a reshape. It won't encourage your hair to grow any faster, but you will find that the removal of split ends improves the overall appearance. Finding a hairdresser who is sympathetic to your cause may take time (try out recommendations from friends) but if you can find one with whom you have a good rapport you can learn a great deal about your hair and how to improve it.

Changing a hairstyle, rather like changing hair colour or having a perm after years of straight hair, takes courage and conviction. See if you can find a wig that will give the same sort of shape that you want. Try it on and it will give you a good idea if the style will work with your body and face shape and whether you will feel comfortable sporting this new look. Even when you have made up your mind, there may be practical limitations which your hair type may impose:

● Thin or fine straight hair easily looks straggly so is best kept short or lightly permed to give more control.

● Medium-textured and straight hair is pretty versatile. It will take a perm if you want curls.

● Fine, curly hair will frizz in humid conditions so will either need a perm to keep the curls in shape or a precise cut to prevent it from looking unruly.

● Coarse hair will respond best to a mid-length cut, since the weight will keep it in check. A short cut will just look bushy.

The Right Hairstyle

High forehead

Large nose

Low forehead

While your hairdresser can advise you about the suitability of your hair for adapting to a style, only you can decide whether it will suit your body size and facial bone structure. The two must be made to balance and a flattering hairstyle can be just the asset you need to direct attention towards your best features. Consider these ideas:

Tall and slim Your height and build need a hairstyle with volume and length which will balance your frame and add a touch of femininity. If left loose the style should aim for fullness, such as that given by soft waves. Alternatively it could be tied back or put up in an elegant fashion. Steer clear of short hair, which will only add emphasis to height.

Tall and big Aim for hair length between shoulder and chin level in a style which softly frames the face or is swept into a chignon with lots of body and fullness. Long voluminous hair will add to your dimensions, while short hair will make you look out of proportion and pin-headed.

Short and plump Too much hair overwhelms the face, yet fullness is important to balance the body. A soft style swept off the neck is good because it elongates the neck and gives an illusion of height. A short, geometric style would be too harsh. Soft body contours need soft hairstyles.

Small and slim Delicate bone structure can be emphasized by very short cuts, either avant-garde, sleek geometric or soft and curly. Hair accentuating the neckline will make a small figure appear taller. Avoid too much volume or too much hair crowding a small face.

Pear-shaped face A wide forehead and a narrow chin needs hair to fill out the area between the shoulders and chin. Don't grow hair past your shoulders or it will emphasize your pointed chin. Hairstyles with forward movement, such as a smooth bob, are ideal.

Short neck

Pear-shape

Long face

Square jaw

Heart-shaped face Most romantic and chignon styles, or those with height, look good with this face shape and balance the wide cheekbones and temples. A wispy fringe also conceals the width of the forehead. Avoid full pageboy fringes or middle partings.

Square face A wide jawline echoes a similar width forehead and the last thing you need is a short, severe haircut to emphasize large features. Soften the square shape with curls or waves directed on to the face or swept off to one side. Avoid a centre parting and a full fringe.

Long, thin face Softness and width is vital to counter the gauntness, so choose a medium-length wavy style or a short one with plenty of curls and waves at cheek level. A soft fringe to one side looks good and reduces forehead depth, but avoid straight hair and a centre parting at all costs.

Round face By creating volume with long wavy hair you are in effect making the face appear smaller, but you must be tall to get away with it. Shorter hairstyles should be kept sleek at the sides and shaped on to the cheek to create a narrowed illusion, while the rest of the hair should be styled with plenty of width across the top.

Low forehead Create an illusion of height by sweeping the hair upwards from the hairline. It is also possible to have a wispy fringe which, if cut in the correct proportion, will disguise the size of the forehead underneath.

High forehead Depending upon the rest of the facial features a soft fringe or light tendrils look best, though if you have breadth as well as height you can take a full fringe.

Small, deepset eyes Choose a short hairstyle which takes the hair up and away from your forehead but allows it to sweep around to your temples, giving the illusion of width.

Short neck It is essential to keep the hair short and shapely or to choose styles which sweep upwards to help give the impression of an elongated neck.

Double-chin It's impossible to conceal the rolls of extra flesh but you needn't accentuate them with short hairstyles which stop at your jawline. Choose a medium-length style below ear level.

Heart-shape

Round face

Double chin

Deep-set eye

Large nose The hair needs softness to counter the unbalanced proportions. Choose a hairstyle with waves or curls, perming if necessary. Never draw attention to the nose by drawing the hair back off the face.

Glasses Frame shapes are just as important as hairstyles and commonsense will tell you that overly big frames will dominate a small face and small frames on a large face will look out of proportion. Your hairstyle must take your frame shape into consideration, so discuss the practical and visual implications with your hairdresser.

Colour Confidence

Wide frames look good on narrow faces

Best for pear-shaped faces

These slim a rounded face

Short noses benefit from a cut-away bridge

This is a good all-round shape – looks best with heart-shaped faces

Changing your hair colour can give your confidence a boost. Covering the grey can make you feel younger, enhancing your natural colour can make you feel brighter and going for a complete change can make you feel like a different person. However, the hair colour you were born with is that which aligns with your complexion, so when you add colour to your hair take your skin tones into account. A drastic switch of colour may mean stepping outside your normal personality and, although it is good to experiment, your most pleasing colour combinations will always be as nature intended!

Choosing a Colour

● If your skin tone is cool and muted your hair may well have been blonde as a child perhaps turning mousy later on in life. Ash blonde colouring will enhance your hair and suit your skin tones, but the grey tone rather than the golden tone is to be preferred. Warm honey and red tones will be ageing and unharmonious.

● If your skin tone is cool and clear your hair will probably be brown or black and may well turn a stunning grey prematurely. If you prefer to cover salt and pepper hair choose ash brown tones, but steer clear of warm browns which mean a reddish tint. For a lighter, softer look, mix ash blonde with brown, remembering that as you age skin tones fade and lighter hair gives a softer effect.

● If your skin tone is warm and muted you probably have blonde or brown hair with natural red tints. Golden blonde tones, auburn, red and warm brown tones will enhance your skin, whereas ash tones will make you look pale and uninteresting. Redheads don't usually suit the salt and pepper effect of white hairs so benefit most from additional colour until their hair has turned completely white.

● If your skin tone is warm and clear your natural hair colouring may well be golden blonde or brown. All manner of warm colours will look good with your skin tones, from flaxen blonde to golden brown and through to strawberry and copper hues. A youthful appearance calls for covering the white hairs until the whole head is completely white and then the effect will be flattering.

Colour Methods

Once you have decided to enhance your hair colouring you must decide whether you want a temporary change, a semi-permanent change or a permanent change, and whether you want to intensify the shade by adding colour or make it paler by removing it. Either way, all of your hair need not be coloured at once, sections can be singled out or highlighted to give a variance of colour, rather like a natural head of hair, which is made up of many different shades of a colour.

Temporary colour The ideal chance to test out a colour to see if you really like the effect. The colourant contains colour molecules which simply cling to the hair cuticle once water has opened it and, as the cuticle is transparent, the colour shows through. A colour rinse will only change the tone of the hair, shading it up or down, and not the actual colour. When the hair is shampooed the cuticles open again and the colour washes out. Colour rinses are an excellent means of experimentation with colour, improving tinted hair between applications and brightening the tone of grey or white hair, but will do nothing to cover it up. Spray-on colours and coloured gels and mousses are also wash-in, wash-out products where the colour just settles on the hair shaft with no penetration at all. Most temporary colours are usually applied after shampooing and are simple to do yourself at home, although you should always read the instructions carefully.

Semi-permanent colour These products contain a medium amount of colour intensity and only penetrate about 20 per cent of the hair cortex, allowing the depth of colour to fade with shampooing over four to six weeks. They don't contain a bleaching agent so will only add colour to your hair. If you want to go lighter, or cover more than a sprinkling of grey hairs, choose a permanent tint. Semi-permanent colourants usually have a built-in conditioner so often add lustre to dull hair. With improved formulas and techniques colouring at home has become easier, though it is still essential to carry out a skin patch test for allergies at least twenty-four hours beforehand and to follow instructions exactly. If in doubt, or if your hair has been damaged by previous do-it-yourself attempts, seek advice from your hairdresser.

Permanent colour Permanent tints, made from a mix of bleach and dye, get right to the heart of the hair, penetrating to the cortex where the natural colour molecules are to be found. There the bleach removes the existing colour, making the cortex porous and ready to absorb the new one. Because the texture of your hair will have a bearing on how readily the tint is accepted, permanent tints are best applied in a salon. Fine hair absorbs colour more easily and coarse hair resists it, but the shade mixes and time processes can be more easily monitored by a professional. Because all permanent colourants have a toxic base a patch test, whether carried out at home or in a salon, is essential.

Bleaching This method strips the natural colour from the hair and gives a solid, white-blonde effect. Unless you are very young this is not flattering and looks highly artificial. However, used in moderation, bleach is a superb method of introducing a natural blonde effect. Highlighting involves singling out strands of hair, either by pulling them through a tightly fitting cap or wrapping them in foil, and painting them with bleach. Tipping or feathering means that just the ends are painted, and streaking involves colouring narrow ribbons of hair which follow the movement of the cut. Applied correctly, bleach will cause no damage to the hair, but over-bleaching makes hair excessively dry, brittle and prone to breakage and split ends.

Vegetable dyes Natural vegetable dyes are non-toxic and, if your skin is sensitive, are a useful alternative to chemical colourants. The colours are less intensive than man-made dyes and do not interfere with the hair's structure. Henna, obtained from the powdered leaves of the henna tree, is probably the best known natural dye. It has been used for centuries and comes in neutral and red. The neutral powder gives a superb conditioning treatment, while the red powder produces varying shades of copper. Red henna works best on dark heads – black, brown and brunette – rather than on grey or blonde, which turn carroty. Herbal dyes are also very popular. Camomile is good for blondes because of its lightening effect; marigold produces a soft, reddish-yellow tone; saffron root a golden tone; sage and walnut infusions both give a brown tone. All will take several applications to achieve the same colour intensity as a chemical tint and, as with the latter, the most successful results will be one or two shades lighter or darker than your natural colouring.

On the Right Wavelength

Forget the frizz – perms aren't like that any more. Formulations loaded with conditioning agents mean that waves and curls are firmly controlled and simply add body to fine hair. However, since the perming process means altering the structure of your hair, and the chemical reshaping will inevitably demoisturize it, it helps to have a healthy head of hair to begin with. No hair should be permed more than three or four times a year; if tinted, it shouldn't be permed within two weeks either side of the colouring process. Hair that is damaged in any other way should not be permed at all. The tightness of the curl depends on the size of the roller that it is wrapped around – the larger the roller, the less curly and the more wavy it will be. Timing is of the essence and, whether the perm is done at home or in the salon, a crucial few minutes can mean the difference between hair that is over-processed and hair that bounces with life.

If you only need to curl it temporarily, use bendy rods while the hair is wet, or heated rollers when it is dry. It's worth remembering, though, that electrical appliances do dry out the hair and, especially after a perm, it's best to avoid even a hairdryer and concentrate on conditioning treatments and regular trims.

Holiday Hair Care

Just as your skin needs extra protection in the sun, so does your hair. Combined with salt, sand, sea water and sea breezes, your hair becomes susceptible to dryness and tangles. Bleached and permed hair is particularly vulnerable as the porous strands lighten and weaken even further under intense sunlight, while tints tend to fade. Chlorinated water from swimming pools as well as salt from the sea can damage hair, making it dry, dull and rough. You can avoid all these hazards if you follow these guidelines:

Hot Tips
● Whenever you are in direct sunlight use a light-coloured scarf or a sun hat to cover your hair.
● When it isn't practical to wear a hat, use a special wet-look gel in your hair. Applied to damp hair, the wax will form a protective coating against the harmful ultra violet light.

● Always use a bathing cap when swimming in a pool or the sea. If you can't bear the thought, comb conditioner through your hair before you plunge in and always try to rinse your hair with fresh water afterwards – even if you have to use a bottle of mineral water.
● Always wash your hair at the end of the day, regardless of whether you have been swimming. The perspiration, sand and salty deposits will need to be cleared from the scalp.
● Condition like crazy!
● Avoid electrical equipment. Finger-dry your hair or, for curls, use bendy rods and then allow to dry naturally.
● If your hair is long keep your cool by plaiting it or pulling it up into a pony tail, otherwise keep it short and simple.

● Even when there is a breeze keeping you cool the sun is still doing its damage, so reduce the tangles by tying your hair up in a scarf, especially if you are on a boat or driving an open-top car.

● A trim and conditioning treatment before you go on holiday will get rid of the split ends and get you off to a good head start.

● Make good use of hair accessories such as clips, slides, hairbands, combs and even fake plaits to keep your hair off your face, but don't use elastic bands – covered bands are best.

The Secrets of Healthy Hair

Keep all hairbrushes and combs scrupulously clean. Wash often in warm water and occasionally use a mild disinfectant to kill bacteria.

● Use pure bristle brushes and avoid sharp, spiky nylon brushes which can tear hair and create split ends. Comb teeth should be rounded and well spaced. Never use a metal or sharp-toothed comb.

● Never lend a brush or comb to someone else.

● To avoid dragging and weakening your hair brush from the ends up, and when blow drying don't pull at the hot hair as you unwind the curl.

● Go easy with hairspray. Too much usage and the build-up is difficult to remove effectively with mild shampoo.

● Tempting mousse can be applied too much. On dry hair it's a temporary rescue act to revive a flagging hairstyle, but heavy usage can take away the natural oil.

● Have your hair trimmed regularly to stop split ends from working up the hair shaft.

● Use a conditioner every time you shampoo.

● Always give your hair a conditioning treatment before and after washing if you have a perm.

● If the style allows it, let your hair dry naturally whenever you have the time.

● Instant cleaning methods don't always mean getting your hair wet. Try this. Cut the foot off a clean, but old, pair of nylon tights. Stretch this over your hair brush and hold it taut. Bend your head so that your hair falls forward and gently brush first one way, then the other. Use long, even strokes for five or ten minutes and you'll find that dust, grime and fluff will cling to the nylon.

● Stimulate the blood flow to the scalp with a massage. Place your fingertips firmly on your scalp and push the skin in rotating circles, slowly moving over the entire head.

● Stick to a well-balanced diet and the end results will be reflected in your hair. Vitamin B-complex is especially good for hair and you can get a good dose from brewer's yeast.

● Always rinse your hair far more than seems necessary, just to be on the safe side, to remove all traces of shampoo. Finish with a cold rinse for really shiny hair.

● Always wash your hair in tepid water, never hot, and squeeze rather than rub at your hair with shampoo.

● Heat and pollution are two of hair's worst enemies. A smoky atmosphere means your hair picks up dirt and starts to look limp, while heat can lead to damaged hair. Shampoo and condition regularly.

● If your scalp shows any signs of disorder go immediately to a registered trichologist.

● Always treat your hair gently, especially when it's wet and liable to stretch.

● Heated rollers and tongs will dry the hair if used too often. Protect the ends of the hair with strips of silver foil.

● Never let your hair become too dirty before washing it.

● If you are trying out a new hairstyle with a parting, make sure the scalp doesn't burn in hot sun.

● Experiment with different hairstyles and accessories, so that even if you keep the length and colour the same you need not get into a rut.

● Cut is the most important aspect of any hairstyle. Make sure the shape suits your face and body and don't be bamboozled into having a new look just because your hairdresser says it's fashionable.

● A good hairdresser will take into account the sort of life you lead when he or she is discussing a positive change of style.

● The state of the hair salon is an indication of whether the inmates will care for your hair in a competent manner. Check that the equipment looks clean, including towels and cover-up capes, and that the floor isn't littered with hair left unswept. A sloppy environment may mean a sloppy hairdresser.

● Any attempts at do-it-yourself hairdressing at home can only be successful if you read the instructions carefully and follow them to the letter. Cut corners at your own risk.

9

MAKE-UP

Women have the perfect weapon when it comes to accentuating their best features. Make-up has given us the freedom to develop our own sense of style and individuality with artful disguise or eye-catching emphasis. Another bonus is that make-up can be a real morale booster (making the effort to look better actually makes you feel better), lifting the spirits of the down-hearted and those laid low by illness. Although in a busy schedule applying make-up may seem like a luxury, there aren't many women who don't build it into their beauty routine. Together with stylish clothes, a flattering hairstyle and a healthy skin, make-up contributes the final polish by simply adding to a sense of self-worth and confidence which stems from knowing you look your best.

Make-up to Flatter Your Skin Tones

A smooth base which is the right texture and colour lays the foundation for a beautiful make-up and becomes the blank canvas on which to create your individual looks. Once you know your skin tone the right colour choice of cosmetics then becomes automatic, not just enhancing your face but harmonizing with your overall appearance.

Your skin tones are determined by three pigments, melanin (brown), carotene (yellow) and haemoglobin (red). Together they combine to give you a cool, blue-based undertone or a warm, yellow-based undertone. As suntans, sallow or ruddy complexions can sometimes cloud the issue, wrists and palms are a more obvious way of studying your true skin tone or otherwise look at your entire body in natural light. If you have freckles, see if they are charcoal brown (cool) or golden brown (warm). Comparisons with other skin tones will help you to decide into which category you fall. To complete the picture you will need to refer to the fashion section in chapters 3 and 4, where further clues are to be found in building up the overall colour identity. Both warm and cool tones are subdivided into muted and clear groups, showing how your colouring relates to the depth and intensity of the blue or yellow-based colours. Here's a summary:

Cool/Clear Characteristics
Skin Very white, white with a delicate pink tone, beige with no cheek colour and inclined to sallowness, rosy beige, olive, black with blue undertone.
Hair Blue-black, medium brown, dark taupe brown, salt and pepper, silver grey or white.
Eyes Black brown, dark brown, hazel, grey blue, dark blue, grey green, green or blue with white flecks or grey rim.

Cool/Muted Characteristics

Skin Pale beige with delicate pink cheeks, pale beige with no cheek colour, very pink, rosy, perhaps with charcoal brown freckles.

Hair Silver blonde, ash blonde, mouse blonde, mouse brown, dark taupe brown, grey brown.

Eyes Cloudy blue with brown or grey flecks or rim, grey blue, grey green, pale grey, blue or green with white flecks and grey rim, hazel, clear blue, pale aqua, soft brown.

Warm/Clear Characteristics

Skin Ivory, sometimes with pale gold freckles, peach, golden beige, rosy cheeks.

Hair Flaxen, golden blonde, strawberry blonde, copper golden brown, auburn, golden grey.

Eyes Clear blue, green, aqua, sometimes with golden or brown flecks, bright blue, light golden brown.

Warm/Muted Characteristics

Skin Ivory, sometimes with freckles, peach, sometimes with golden freckles, golden beige, dark beige, golden black.

Hair Red, coppery red brown, golden or chestnut brown, golden blonde, treacle brown-black, golden grey.

Eyes Dark brown, golden brown, amber, hazel, clear green or with brown or gold flecks, blue with a turquoise tone.

Cool Complexions

Find a foundation that suits your complexion and you'll find that the subtle nuance of a warm or cool base will set the perfect tone for all the other colours you may use on your face. A rose base suitable for cool complexions has a purplish or pink cast, compared side by side with a warm yellow base which will then appear obviously peachy or yellow beige.

● Cool/muted skin tones benefit from a base with a hint of pink. If your complexion is ruddy choose a beige foundation, derived from rose, but with no noticeable pink in it.

● Cool/clear skin tones, often white, beige or olive, need a beige foundation with a pink undertone. A wrong-coloured beige foundation will succeed in making cool skin look sallow, while a peachy colour will appear a dirty orange tone.

Warm Complexions

Yellow-based foundations are often called natural, ivory, peach, golden or copper.

● Warm/muted skin tones look best in ivory, peach or copper shades. Natural beige skins can have added warmth with a peach cheek colour, while a sallow skin improves with a peach base.

● Warm/clear skin tones look best in light to dark peach foundations or pale ivory with an additional peach blusher. High colouring benefits from a natural beige base to tone down the warmth, but blue-pink foundations should be avoided at all times.

Base Facts

● Experiment with different foundation colours. You can mix two together to get the perfect match, making your base slightly darker if you are tanned for summer.

● There is no rule that says you must wear foundation, but it does act as a protection against pollution in the air. During summer months, provided your skin is good, a tinted moisturizer or coloured gel may be sufficient.

● Shop lighting can distort colour, so when you buy foundation try to look at it (testing it if possible) against your jawline in natural daylight.

● Choose a foundation of a texture which suits your skin type. Medicated foundations are fine for spot-prone skin; anti-shine, water-based matt foundations are best for greasy skins. Liquids in bottles and tubes suit most skin types and give light coverage. The all-in-one make-up which includes base and powder gives a good matt finish but can be a bit drying. Dry skins (and more mature skins, which may need more coverage) should try foundation creams from a pot, stick foundations or cake in a compact.

● Always apply foundation over clean, moisturized skin which has had a few minutes to settle. Never layer your foundation over stale make-up.

● Use your fingertips to dot the foundation over the central areas of your face before using a damp sponge to give a thin, even coverage. Work from the centre of the face outwards to avoid a mainline build-up.

● Blending is the secret of a smooth foundation and will ensure that you don't have any obvious tidemarks. Take the foundation over the eyelids and below the jawline around to the neck. A sponge is pliable and gets into the crevices, but finish off by smoothing with your fingertips.

● If you have a small blemish or shadows under the eyes which need covering use a concealer or a light-coloured cream foundation. Dot the concealer in the required place with a fingertip or small brush and blend, using delicate pressure.

Face Faults

It is possible to use shading as a means of minimizing some facial faults. A darker foundation makes a feature recede, while a highlight does the opposite – but don't overdo it or you will just draw attention to what you are trying to hide. It is better to emphasize all your good points than to try to disguise something that probably only you notice.

To slim down a wide nose Blend a darker shade of foundation down each side of the nose, starting at the bridge and blending outwards using a wedge-shaped piece of sponge, fingertips or a soft, flat brush.

To straighten a crooked nose Apply a darker foundation on the bumpy side of a crooked nose and a lighter shade on the opposite side to help balance the bump.

To shorten a long nose Blend darker foundation around the nostrils and just under the tip.

To minimize a double chin or heavy jawline Use a darker foundation to contour the jawline and blend into the neck. Use a lighter shade on the pad of the chin to make it more prominent.

Blusher

Round face

Square face

Heart-shaped face

Subtlety is the key word when it comes to colour and contour, building up the blush to the right strength and blending away hard edges. A blusher is what makes a face 'come alive' and can be applied in cream form (compact, stick or pencil) or powder (generally packaged with its own applicator). Choose from shades of peach and tan for warm skin tones and all shades of pink for cool ones. As a general rule of thumb, the softer your colouring, the softer the shade of blusher.

Cream blusher Good for dry skins and complexions that just need a natural sheen. Apply sparingly after you have blended in your foundation and before you use powder to finish off. Blending with fingertips or a sponge ensures that there are no patches of obvious colour. On some skins cream blusher may 'sink in' or need strengthening after you have finished the rest of your make-up. In this case you must add more colour with a powder blusher in a similar shade.

Powder blusher Applied after you have powdered your foundation, powder blusher is easy to control and gives a very soft effect. Don't put too much blusher on your brush and tap the brush on the back of your hand to remove surplus. Remember, you can always add more to strengthen your colour but it is difficult to remove too much. Mature skins will benefit from soft, matt colours and should avoid frosted blushers, which can look like glistening perspiration.

Long face

...ear shape for oval
...ce

Artful Shaping

Where to apply blusher? Simply press your thumb just underneath your cheekbone, place your finger actually on the bone and imagine a teardrop shape on your cheek, with the rounded end nearest your nose but no further in than the middle of your eyes. Always add colour sparingly, blending well and keeping it away from your hairline. A blusher should never look like a streak at the side of your face – it should be barely noticeable, just a tinge of colour contouring your cheeks and enhancing your face. Blusher outline can be adjusted slightly to improve a face shape. Here's how:

● A crescent of colour slims down a round face and narrows a square jawline.

● A triangle of colour emphasizes the cheekbone on a heart-shaped face and creates a horizontal effect to shorten a long one.

Powder

A dusting of powder helps to set your make-up, gives a smooth, even finish to your complexion, covers the shine from oil-prone areas of forehead and centre panel and helps to stop cream eye shadows and pencils from creasing. Compacts of pressed powder are best for retouching during the day, otherwise use loose powder. A fine, loose, translucent, colourless powder looks soft and natural and is applied after your foundation and any other cream-based cosmetics that you may use – such as blusher or eye shadow creams – and before you use any powder eye shadows or powder blusher.

● Transparent powder will lighten your foundation fractionally, whereas a tinted powder may alter the colour of any make-up underneath.

● Using a powder puff, press the powder firmly on the face and neck, one area at a time. Concentrate on the central areas of your face. Now use a fat complexion brush to whisk away any surplus, working with downward strokes to prevent powder settling into fine lines around the eyes and getting caught up in fine facial hairs.

● Check that powder is well blended over the face and that there are no shiny or caked patches, especially around the nostrils and chin area.

Eye Make-up

Sparkling eyes are easily the most noticeable feature of your face, communicating as they do your emotions and reflecting intelligence. Even cleverly applied make-up, however, cannot disguise puffiness through lack of sleep or bloodshot eyes from an excess of smoking and alcohol. Focus on some basic eye care and healthy-looking, expressive eyes will be easily enhanced with some creative and imaginative eye make-up techniques.

Eye Colours

Eye shadow should set off the shape and colour of your eyes, not your dress, so choose warm or cool colours according to your skin tone and don't pick a shade that matches your eye colouring exactly. The iris is generally composed of several colours, so if you have flecks of gold, brown, grey or green, these shades will look good automatically.

● Pale colours are useful highlighters. Matt or gloss, they 'open' out an area and are used on the browbone beneath the eyebrow. A dot of pale shadow just above the lashes at the centre of your eyelids also widens eyes.

● Darker colours are used to contour the eyes and serve to intensify the shape.

● All colours should be blended together so that there are no harsh edges. Use cosmetic brushes and sponge-tipped applicators to reach the awkward corners where fingertips become clumsy.

● Keep all brushes and applicators very clean to avoid eye infections.

● If your eyelids are at all crêpey avoid shiny eye shadows, which just emphasize the point.

Eyeliner

The liquid type comes in a multitude of colours and is applied to the top of the lashes with a fine brush. Soft colours work well but dark colours can look hard. An eyeliner pen gives more precision and is easier to control. Cake eyeliner is coloured powder used with water and the line can be softened afterwards by smudging with a cotton bud. Always work from the centre of the eye to the outside corner, supporting your elbow on a flat surface for a steady hand. Extend the line past the outer corner of the eye for a dramatic, stylized effect, or stop at the outer corner for a round, wide-eyed effect. Eye pencils can be used in the same way as a liquid eyeliner, but give a much softer, more natural line. The pencils must be soft to prevent them dragging the skin – warm them up on a radiator, if necessary. Kohl pencils can give extra definition inside the lower lash line. A colour which reflects the eye colour can look sensational, or try a white pencil to widen the eye.

Mascara

Experiment with the wand mascaras to see which suits you best. You'll find thick and thin brushes, waterproof and non-waterproof varieties and mascara with extra fibres to lengthen and thicken the eyelashes. Coat both top and bottom of the upper lashes, starting at the roots and working towards the tips, looking down into a mirror held at chin level. Then hold the mirror up and keep your chin down to mascara the lower lashes. Allow the mascara to dry between coats (two or three coats are sufficient). Brush the lashes with a clean mascara brush to keep them well separated. Coloured mascara adds emphasis to the eye, especially if it tones with your own eye colouring. Softer colours look best with blonder hair and fair skins. Darker, dramatic colours flatter brunettes with darker skin colouring.

Eyebrows

These make the perfect frame for your eyes and balance your features. Thin eyebrows look hard and unflattering, while heavy, straight eyebrows tend to dominate the face and detract from the eyes. Drastic reshaping is often a mistake but you can tidy up straggly brows. Tweeze them into shape using short, quick movements in the direction of the hair growth. Always pluck from beneath and pull the skin taut between thumb and forefinger, holding the tweezers in the other hand ready to grip each hair as close as possible to the root. A good guide to correct proportions is to take a pencil and hold it in a straight line from the side of the nostril and past the inner corner of the eye. Where it touches the eyebrow is your starting point. Now angle the pencil so that it skims the outer corner of your eye. Where it touches the eyebrow is the point at which it should finish. The highest point of your eyebrow should be directly above your iris when you look straight ahead. If your eyebrows are thin and need additional filling in, use a soft eye pencil in a suitable colour or eyebrow powder and a fine brush. With short, feathery strokes, gently add colour against the direction of growth. You'll find this is a more subtle method than if you follow the hair direction. Finally, brush the eyebrows through with a clean brush.

Optical Illusions

With some skilful shading the eyes can appear to change shape. Here's how:

Small or close-set eyes Pluck your eyebrows finely to give maximum eye area. Then use a pale shadow on the browbone, plus a little on the lid to attract light to the eyes. Use a deeper colour shadow in the eye socket, taking the colour round and under the lower eyelashes and also winging out at the sides. Mascara both upper and lower lashes, using two coats on the upper lashes only. Emphasize

Deep-set eyes

Narrow lids

Small, close-set eyes

Droopy lids

Overhanging brow

the outer half of the eye with a soft pencil.

Narrow lids Use a barely-there pale shadow all over the lid and then use a deeper shadow in the socket line, following the natural curve of the eye, then taking colour around and under the eye before finally fading on to the browbone.

Deep-set eyes Apply a pale shadow all over the area from lashes to browbone, concentrating colour on the eyelid. Use a white pencil on the inner rim of the lower eye.

Droopy lids Counter the downturn by concentrating eye shadows in an upswept movement on to the browbone at the outer edges. Mascara the top lashes only and use eyelash curlers to make them curl upwards.

Overhanging brow Use a medium shadow on the lid and then blend in a pale eye shadow above the socket line and on to the brow, winging upwards and outwards.

Eye-Deals

● Use good-quality sable hair brushes to blend your powder eye shadows.

● Take a tip from the professional make-up artists and place a tissue under your lower eyelashes while you are applying shadows to catch any 'bits'.

● Test colours on the backs of your hands and blend if necessary, shaking off excess powder shadows.

● Keep eyeliner to a subtle definition by drawing a thin line close to the eyelash roots and then blend with a cotton bud to soften.

● Keep all eye pencils sharpened to a good point for easier control.

● Cotton buds are an excellent way of removing eye shadow mistakes or a mascara smudge from the skin.

● For extra-curly lashes, use an eyelash curler before applying mascara.

● Three thin coats of mascara are infinitely preferable to one thick globby layer!

● For women in a hurry, fair lashes can be tinted at a salon once every six weeks to give the same effect as mascaraed lashes. Then all you have to do is tip them with Vaseline every morning.

● For a glamorous change, use a brown or black mascara and then tip the end with a colour like bright blue, green or gold.

Eye Care ● Soothe your eyes with a refreshing eye bath. You can buy an eye cup and refreshing lotion from most chemists.

● Relax your eyes with ice-cold pads soaked in eye lotion and put your feet up for ten minutes.

● Add a sparkle to your eyes with eye drops.

● Use a special eye cream around your eyes at night to help keep wrinkles at bay. Use a gentle fingertip movement to massage it in.

● Roll your eyes around as a relaxing exercise.

● Always wear protective sunglasses in strong sunlight.

● Don't wait for headaches and watery eyes before you visit an optician. Get your eyes checked regularly, especially as you get older.

● If you wear glasses it's important to wear eye make-up in order to bring your eyes into prominence. Use hypo-allergic products on sensitive eyes.

● Choose frames according to your skin tone and they'll blend in with your overall appearance; warm tones look good in creams, beiges, sand, amber and tortoiseshell, cool tones look good in pale greys, blues and taupe – black frames are too hard.

● If glasses don't appeal, take advice about contact lenses. These are wafer-thin circles of a special transparent material, precision made to fit over the cornea. They are the nearest thing to perfect vision for those who suffer from short or long sightedness. They can even intensify the colour of your own eyes so that they become a beautiful feature instead of a corrective necessity.

Lipstick If nothing else is used in the way of make-up, lipstick remains a symbol of femininity and a fast way of adding colour to the face, either used conventionally on the lips or as a cream rouge on the cheeks. My own feeling is that if you don't have time to apply a lipstick properly, don't do it at all – just use a lipgloss. Like the rest of your make-up, lip colours must complement your natural skin tones; fair hair and fair skins suit the paler, warm pinks, peaches and coral colours (warm skin tones) or chalky blue-pinks and rose pinks (cool skin tones) while darker looks are suitably the deeper terracottas and flame reds (warm) or plums, burgundies and ruby reds (cool).

Perfect Lip Colour

● Use your foundation to cover the entire mouth area to act as a base.

● Use a slim, sharpened lip pencil in a similar colour to your lipstick to draw an outline. For the top lip, start at the centre and work out towards the corner of the mouth. For the lower lip, work from side to side.

● Use a lipbrush to take colour from the lipstick. A narrow, flat-ended brush will give you a good shape and more control than applying the lipstick direct to your lips.

● Fill in by stroking colour on to the top lip, starting at the centre and working outward.

● Blot by folding a clean tissue in half and placing it between your lips. Press lightly together to remove excess lipstick. Finish with a lip gloss, but don't take it right to the mouth edge as it can cause lipstick to run.

Quick Tips

● **The fastest way to apply lipstick is to use a lip pencil as opposed to a lipliner pencil. These will outline and fill in all at once. Use a wand gloss applicator for speedy shine.**

● More mature skins will have tiny lines around the mouth which sometimes appear to be 'bleeding' from the lipstick. In this case, outline the lips with pencil and blot with a tissue. Keeping the lips together, smile and pat the edges of your mouth very lightly with a little loose powder applied with a cotton bud. Then fill in with your normal colour, ensuring that you don't go to the very edge of the lips. Finally, blot again very lightly.

● **Keep the lips in good condition by smoothing in a little Vaseline at night. It also makes an inexpensive lip gloss.**

● Keep lipsticks in a cool place. When you are in a hot country they are liable to melt in the sun.

● **Use a magnifying mirror in a good light for best application results.**

● Steady your elbow on a solid surface when you are drawing your outline.

● **Don't apply too much colour – it accentuates the cracks.**

● Bright mouth colours draw attention to your teeth. Make sure they are up to it!

● **Natural colours look good by day but try some shimmer at night. A gold or silver highlighter in the centre of a bottom lip or used just on the bow of the lips can look sensational.**

● Altering your lip shape is possible with clever use of a lipliner pencil. Here's how:

Thin lips Take the pencil just outside the natural lipline and add a highlight to the upper lip.

Full lips Take the pencil just inside the natural lipline, use medium-toned lipstick colours and no shine.

Crooked lips Use your lipliner pencil to balance out the shape, adjusting the line either just above or below your natural lipline.

Shapeless lips Start with a good base of foundation lightly dusted with powder and then draw in a new shape with lipliner pencil, giving a good cupid bow and more fullness on the bottom lip. Fill in with a medium-toned lipstick.

Thin lips

Full lips

Crooked lips

Shapeless lips

Does Your Face Date You? The way you make up your face can reveal it all too glaringly if you are stuck in a time warp. Think of the fifties and there is the powdered, pale face, the beauty spot and the dark, exaggerated eyebrows. Think of the sixties and imagine pale lips and exaggerated eye make-up complete with heavy socket line and fake lashes. Think of the seventies and the china doll make-up with rainbow eyeshadows and plucked eyebrows. Think of the eighties and think of variety – from healthy, outdoor, natural make-up to stunning soapstar glamour. The secret of an up-to-date face is adaptability.

● Don't be afraid to experiment with new techniques, new colours, new ideas.

● Keep your eye on the cosmetic counters and the beauty magazines to see what's new.

● Have your face professionally made-up occasionally, and learn from the experts.

● Save time by keeping all your favourite make-up and tools together on a small tray.

● Never try any new make-up techniques or colours just before you have to look wonderful. Test anything new when you have the time to experiment.

● Make use of applicators. Make-up is more controlled, hygenic and goes on with a light touch.

● Make up in a good light. By daylight, turn your back to a window and face a mirror which reflects the daylight. Make sure artificial light is even, not coming from above or from one side.

● To let make-up 'settle' easily, wait five or ten minutes after moisturizing before applying it to cool skin.

● If you change your hairstyle or your hair colour reassess your make-up.

● As you mature, be alert to changes in your complexion. Review your foundation colour every few years. As skin tones lighten, you may need to switch to a softer shade.

● Always keep blusher subtle to avoid a painted look and as you age soften all the make-up colours together.

● Natural liplines tend to fade with age, so use a soft lip pencil to give definition and always wear lipstick.

● Remember that you can always add colour, whereas it is hard to remove an over-zealous amount. Err on the side of caution and practice will make perfect.

10

THE FINISHING

TOUCHES

Details count! Just as a ladder in your tights or worn-down heels detract from your dress, so, too, do chewed-up fingernails or chipped nail polish. It's worth spending a few extra minutes getting things right. Happy feet means an easy walk and good posture. Cared-for hands means they are less ageing. Even your perfume can add to your persona by leaving behind a lasting impression. Don't miss out on the finishing touches if you want to win friends and influence people!

Hand and Nail Care

Apart from the face, hands are the most continuously exposed and abused parts of the body, making them an age giveaway unless cared for properly. Water, weather extremes, dirt, detergents and potential allergens are all reasons why hand and nail problems occur with regular monotony. Counteract with common sense and you'll soon be rewarded with smooth hands and good-looking nails.

Handy Hints
● Use a mild or unperfumed soap when you wash your hands. Use a nail brush to scrub gently over the knuckles and nails.
● Always wash soap off with clear running water and pat the hands dry, especially between the fingers and under rings which can act as a trap for moisture, soap and detergents.
● Vegetable, fruit or nicotine stains should be rubbed with lemon juice, followed by a rinse and an application of hand cream.
● Engrained dirt can be removed with a little olive oil poured into the palm with a teaspoon of sugar. Rub into the hands, working it in thoroughly, and then rinse and dry.
● Hand creams are designed to moisturize and protect your skin, so it makes sense to have them strategically placed around the house, especially near wash basins, so that you will remember to use them.
● Like skin care products, hand creams are not necessarily better for being expensive. Try out several brands and see whether creams, gels or lotions are most effective on your skin.
● Pamper your hands with an occasional mask, just as you would your face, to improve colour and texture. Soften them once in a while by slathering them in hand cream or Vaseline and go to bed wearing an old pair of cotton gloves. Overnight the intensive treatment works wonders, though I would recommend doing this only when your husband is away!
● Always use rubber gloves for heavy-duty household

chores, especially if you use strong cleaning agents, and remember to remove rings first.

● Always use gloves for washing-up, gardening, painting and decorating. Turn them inside out after use to avoid the dampness that causes bacteria to collect.

● When the sun shines use a sun-screen on your hands, just as you would on your face.

● Protect your hands against the bitter cold with warm gloves. Stimulate the circulation and improve flexibility with a few exercises. Clench your hands into fists then fling them open, spreading the fingers as wide as possible. Now make wide circles with each thumb and finger in turn. Finally, let your hands go floppy at the wrists, rotating them in loose circles, first clockwise and then anti-clockwise.

Nail Tales

Although nails appear to be tough and durable, their structure and growth pattern makes them extremely vulnerable. The visible surface of nails is made up of several layers of dead tissue which are bonded by particles of oil and moisture and toughened by keratin, a protein substance which also makes up the surface of our outer skin and hair.

The living nail, or matrix, where cells are nourished from blood capillaries and nerve ends, extends below the cuticle – a fold of skin dividing the nail from the rest of the finger – and is only visible as the whitish half-moon, or lunula, at the base of the nail.

Common nail disorders such as ridges, white marks, grooves and furrows increase with advancing years and often form from barely noticeable knocks and scrapes, but these will be enough to damage the area around the matrix where the cells are being formed. Apart from external carelessness, your nails also reflect internal changes in the body's metabolism and chemistry. Emotional shock, stress, drugs (including the pill) and pregnancy could all be recorded as blemishes in the nails, though a time lag may not

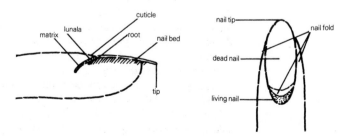

make it immediately obvious. The average nail grows only 1mm a week and it takes approximately six months for a nail to grow out fully.

Breaking Points
Brittle nails are often the result of an imbalanced diet or hormonal changes. Green vegetables, raw vegetables, especially carrots and tomatoes, vitamin A-rich yellow and red fruits, salads, skimmed milk, yoghurt, fish, lean meat, liver, wholegrains and wheatgerm oil, rich in vitamin E, provide the essential nutrients for healthy eating and healthy nail formation. Any deficiency in zinc, vitamin B6, sulphur, iodine, iron, calcium and protein tends to eventually make nails too soft or too brittle.

If you are unhappy with the state of your nails supplement your diet with brewer's yeast, which is rich in vitamin B-complex, cod-liver oil, rich in vitamin A, and kelp, for a generous helping of iodine.

Help your nails externally by keeping them away from water and detergents and massage in special nail treatment creams. Cuticles and soft, flaking nails will also benefit from these creams. Help is also on hand for nail biters. It's an unattractive habit which leaves the nail with frail, ragged edges. Special bitter-tasting anti-biting lotions are available to paint on the nails which help to discourage the avid nail biter.

Nail Tips
● Keep the nails short and softly squared until they have stopped splitting and flaking before attempting to grow them long.

● Carry an emery board around in your purse to smooth away nail snags quickly before a catch pulls the whole tip off.

● File your nails with the fine side of an emery board at an angle of 45° from just underneath the nail, working from the edge towards the middle. Don't file right into the corners. Finish by smoothing the nail, holding the board upright and stroking lightly in a downwards direction only.

● Never file your nails after a shower or bath. They will be too soft and you will risk splitting them.

● Don't clean under your nails with a sharp metal instrument. Try a well-soaped sponge or a wooden manicure stick wrapped around with cotton wool.

● Use a pencil to dial telephone numbers and invest in a metal letter opener to deal with the post.

● Nail polish can help strengthen and protect nails. Touch up chips as they occur, and if you do a weekly manicure add another coat of polish midweek for lasting colour.

● Use the minimum of nail polish remover because it is drying and choose a conditioned oily remover, not acetone. Never pick off old nail polish, as you remove a layer of nail each time.

● A quick alternative to polishing your nails is to buff them with a chamois leather buffer to improve circulation and shine, moving in one direction only, from the base to the tip.

● If the whites of your nails still don't look clean, even after scrubbing them, try applying a white pencil to the underside of the nails to boost whiteness.

● Nail polish colours come in every hue imaginable, but stick with colours that harmonize with your skin tones. Warm tones go for yellow-based colours – peach, corals, warm pinks – while cool tones go for rose pinks with blue undertones. The darker your skin, the more intense the colours should be. Frosted colours will show up more imperfections in the nail than cream polishes.

The Perfect Manicure

1. Remove old polish with cotton wool.
2. File the nails into a pretty shape, using an emery board.
3. Soak the nails in a bowl of warmed oil before cleaning up the tips.
4. Apply cuticle remover to soften the cuticles and ease them back from the nail plate using a rubber hoof or orange stick wrapped in cotton wool.
5. Tissue off excess oil and apply a base coat to prevent staining.
6. Apply the nail polish. Paint the middle of the nail first and then fill in the base and round and up either side with the second and third strokes. To make nails look longer, don't take the colour right to the edges of the sides. Several thin coats are much better than one thick layer, but make sure that the polish is properly dry between coats.
7. Apply a colourless top coat or sealer, taking it along and under the tip of the nail to seal in the polish and help prevent chipping. Spray nails with a quick-dry spray. The surface of the nails will feel dry after about ten minutes, but the layers will not be really hard for several hours. For most women this is an impossibly long period in which to take care that they are not scraped or dented, so it makes sense to do them before going to bed and let them harden overnight.

Fingertip fact Applying nail polish can't be done in a hurry! If time is short, don't risk smudged polish but use a coat of clear varnish for instant shine. If your nails are short or unsightly don't risk colour at all, just buff them to a natural sheen. Alternatively, invest in some fake nails while yours are growing underneath.

The perfect
pedicure

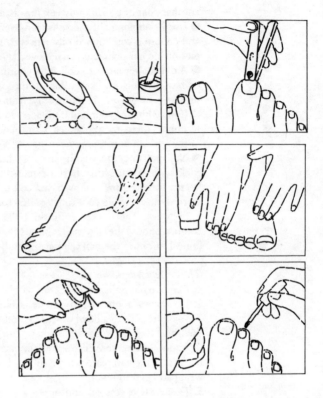

Caring For Your Feet

Considering the amount of time that we spend on them, we don't really notice our feet very much. Hidden away in shoes, they usually only get some attention if something starts to hurt. Most of our problems stem from wearing unsuitable shoes – and over the years there have been some painful fashions, from winkle-pickers to platforms. Nowadays, thankfully, it is much easier to get good shoes that fit – and if they don't you'll know all about it. When your feet hurt, you hurt all over. Pressure on the nerves of your feet can give you backache, a headache and pains in other parts of your body, not to mention the fatigue and nervous strain which will show in your face. Follow these guidelines and you'll find yourself walking effortlessly, walking tall.

Foot facts

● Buy shoes that fit properly. They should be snug at the heel and instep and about ½ inch (1 cm) longer than your foot. The uppers should preferably be made of soft supple leather or fabric and the sole should be as wide as your foot, with the widest part at the first joint of your big toe.

● When you try on a new pair make sure you stand up and walk in them. As soon as you stand, your feet spread. They also swell slightly as the daily pressures take their toll, so try to shop for new shoes at the end of the day to be sure of a comfortable fit.

● Posture is important, as it affects the way the body distributes its weight. You should stand and walk with your feet parallel and your toes pointing straight ahead for even distribution over the feet. If you don't, the weight of the body is thrown onto the inner border of the feet, which will weaken feet and ankles and strain calf muscles.

● Vary the height of the heels you wear and be aware that very high heels will throw the weight of the body off-balance. Heels no longer than 2 inches (5 cm) are reckoned to be best, with a soft cushioned sole to protect against hard pavements. At home, slip into something flat or go barefoot for a change.

● Never neglect minor foot problems as, untreated, they could develop into something much worse. Danger signals are hard skin anywhere: corns caused by tight shoes are easily removed but can recur unless you change your footwear. A burning sensation on the ball of the foot may be a callous. Itchy toes, split skin between them and blisters underneath mean athlete's foot; the big toe leaning towards the others, the start of a bunion.

● Home solutions involve a pumice stone. It's the gentlest way to remove corns, callouses and dead skin build-up. Saturate the pumice while you are soaking your feet in warm salty water. Then rub a little hand lotion on the pumice and work the stone across rough areas in one direction only. If the symptoms don't clear, see a chiropodist.

● Flexercise: Each foot has some 26 bones, 82 ligaments, 20 muscles and 33 joints arranged in two main arches to make three weight-bearing points; one at the heel, one at the base of the little toe and one at the base of the great toe. Obviously this complex structure benefits from exercise. Try these simple movements. Standing barefoot, keep your heel on the ground as you flex your foot, pointing your toes up

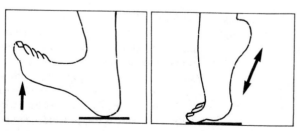

A simple foot exercise

towards the ceiling as far as you can go. Hold for five seconds then lower your foot to the floor. Transfer your weight to your toes and press down, raising your heels off the floor and arching your feet. Repeat six times. From a sitting position, alternately point your toes up towards the ceiling then curl them down. Repeat ten times.

● To relax tired, aching feet and puffy ankles, lie flat on the floor with your feet above your head, supported against a wall. Close your eyes and relax for ten minutes.

● Massage your feet with body lotion when they are tired. Hold the foot in both hands and press the sole firmly with the thumbs along its length, especially on the ball of the foot. Massage all round each toe, using small circular movements and finishing by gently pulling each one. Then work your way back and massage around the ankles and up towards the calf.

● Treat yourself to a weekly pedicure. Here's how:

1. Begin with clean, washed feet and dry well, especially between the toes. Use the towel to push back softened cuticles.

2. Use nail clippers to cut tough toenails and always clip them straight across the top as curving the corners can lead to ingrowing toenails.

3. Tackle hard skin with a pumice stone and then massage in body lotion.

4. Spray the feet with anti-perspirant or a foot-cooling spray.

5. If you want to paint your toenails use a base and top coat just as you would for a manicure, but remember to separate your toes with cotton wool to prevent the nail polish from smudging.

Footnote Sweaty feet? Always use an anti-perspirant spray after washing your feet and shake talcum powder into your shoes to help absorb moisture. Sweat from feet has no smell but bacteria breeding in warm, dark shoes do cause odour. Wearing deodorized insoles inside your shoes can help.

A Fresh Approach

Confidence comes with looking good, feeling good and smelling fresh. Washing the body in a daily bath or shower frees the pores from sweat and oily sebum which are secreted from glands in the skin. Neither sweat nor sebum smells unpleasant in itself – in fact, the faintly salty smell of sweat on the skin can be healthy and attractive. However, when air cannot circulate freely over the surface of the skin because of clothes, moisture is trapped and cannot evaporate, bacteria attacks and an unpleasant odour is the result.

Bath Beautifiers

The quickest and most effective way of cleansing your body is to have a shower and soap away daily grime. Showers invigorate and pep up your circulation, while baths tend to be relaxers. Never have water too hot and add a cup of vinegar to soften hard bath water. Add some oil or a cup of powdered milk if you have dry skin. Herbs wrapped up in muslin are a popular addition to bath water – mint and rosemary for stimulation, camomile and thyme for soothing qualities and lavender if you want to smell beautiful.

Splash Down

After your bath or shower close the pores with a splash of cold water then use a large, thick towel for the most effective rub-down. Talcum powder smells nice, helps you slide into clothes and is soothing and absorbent, but is no substitute for thorough drying with a towel. Body lotion or baby oil will replace lost moisture and is particularly effective on areas like elbows, knees and feet. It also gives you a chance to massage any podgy areas like thighs and buttocks to help get the circulation moving. Wait until you have cooled down before applying a deodorant or anti-perspirant.

Sticky Situations

Perspiring is a normal bodily function and is the natural cooling system. A change in body temperature brought about by a hot day, a stuffy office, an energetic sports activity, a high fever or a spicy curry can activate the eccrine sweat glands. The apocrine sweat glands respond to emotional and nervous change. The water produced evaporates from the body and acts to cool it down. The high percentage of glands concentrated in the armpits are usually the most active during the day and give rise to the use of deodorants, which mask unpleasant smells, or anti-perspirants, which curb wetness.

Smooth Coverage

Roll-on deodorants and anti-perspirants are economical and long-lasting. They can be applied directly to the skin and are considered to be more effective than the spray-on types. Roll-ons are, however, used much more effectively if your armpits are free from hair, since sweat clings to hair and evaporates less easily. If you do prefer to leave it underarm hair will absorb perspiration, but essential hygiene dictates frequent washing combined with a spray anti-perspirant. If you wish to remove hair quickly shaving is a popular method, and you can razor off hairs on the legs at the same time for smooth bare limbs during the summer months.

Waxing can do the same job – good for legs but not recommended for underarms, as it is too painful. Depilatory products are an alternative method and literally melt the hair down to where it emerges from the skin. Always do a patch test in case your skin is sensitive to a product and, as with shaving, never use a deodorant or anti-perspirant immediately after removing hair since the skin will be tender.

Beat the Heat
Keep cool by choosing clothes loose enough to allow air to circulate and which have armholes deep enough to be roomy. Natural fibres are best because, unlike man-made fabrics, they allow moisture to evaporate easily. Keep calm in a heated situation by taking deep, relaxing breaths. Pace yourself as you move around and stop hurrying. Run your wrists under cold water for a few minutes for instant relief and use an eau de toilette cooling spray, which has a high alcohol content and evaporates quickly from your skin.

Good Scents
● Layer perfume for longer-lasting freshness. Use perfumes in the same family – body lotions, talc, toilet water – at bath time. Later add the perfume concentrate to pulse points. Stroke these areas during the day to release new waves of scent – it keeps the fragrance going for hours.
● Body hot spots are the pulse points, the warmth of which promotes the power of your perfume. Pulse points are found on the inner wrist, crook of the elbow, back of the knee and the throat.
● Never buy a fragrance because it smells good on somebody else. It's your own body chemistry that gives you an individual aroma.
● When buying perfume never test more than three at one session because your nose suffers from smell fatigue after a while.
● Don't sniff from the bottle as you will only smell the top note. For the full fragrance test on your wrist, wait a few minutes and then you will get the lingering effect.
● You can pay through the nose for a designer label. Experiment with your own perfume by buying widely available and inexpensive perfume oils and mixing your own concoction. Oils last longer on the skin and can be added to your bath water, your room, by pouring a drop into some water and leaving a dish on your radiator, and even to your washing machine programme for beautiful smelling clothes.
● Keep fragrance in a cool, dark place. Light can cause a chemical reaction and change the nature of the perfume. Keeping it in its cartons helps.

● Provided perfume is well sealed and well stored it should last for about a year, but always replace the cap as soon as the perfume has been used or it will evaporate quickly.

● Never decant perfume into a plastic bottle – it's better to go for a small purse-sized atomizer for travelling.

● Don't wear perfume in strong sunlight as it can provoke allergic reactions.

● If you can't wear perfume on your skin because it is sensitive lightly mist your hair, as hair attracts fragrance and holds it for hours. You can also spray lingerie lace, fabric coat hangers, your ironing board before ironing clothes and even your pillow case for the sweetest of dreams!

Special Occasions

Special occasions need extra preparations on both the fashion and beauty front. The outfit you will choose to wear for an occasion will naturally depend on the nature of the event. Get all the details in your mind in advance to avoid a last-minute panic.

Wedding Guest

Hat Essential! The perfect finishing touch to your outfit and your chance to show your individuality – but be reasonably restrained, since the bride should be the focus of attention, not you. Choose a brimmed hat for a softer look, a turban for sophistication.

Hair Styled to suit the hat. Take the hat along to your hairdresser and combine your ideas – or experiment at home, but don't let your hair become an afterthought.

Make-up Waterproof mascara is essential to counter the odd tear that may escape! Lipstick is important to keep the face in balance, especially with a hat adding extra interest, but blot well, bearing in mind the inevitable hugs and kisses. Perfume, not lipstick, is the key to making your mark.

Jewellery Keep it discreet and preferably real. Rings are the thing!

Outfit Bear in mind that churches are cool and receptions are warm, so a dress and jacket is ideal. The style needn't be too formal but do choose luxury fabrics like silk and fine wool because they always hold their shape well.

Gloves If you feel happy wearing them that's fine, but there are no rules to say you must. Tone them with your outfit rather than use a contrast colour, though.

Tights Nothing flamboyant. Choose flesh tones.

Shoes Stick to a medium-heel, neutral-coloured court shoe which will blend in with your tights.

Summer Social Event

Hat You could really go to town with an extravaganza here but big hats block the view and won't win you many friends at Ascot, so think carefully about the shape. Hatpins are essential if you want to hang on to it.

Hair A hat will keep your hair in place, but if you don't want to wear one choose some form of hair decoration and use plenty of hairspray.

Make-up You must apply make-up to last all day, but no harsh colours. Natural daylight is forgiving – but not that forgiving! Aim for harmony with your outdoor setting.

Jewellery Ostentatious jewellery is out on this occasion. Pearls are the answer.

Outfit Here's your chance to stand out from the crowd if you so desire. Splash out with some colour – a print dress or a two-piece worn with a contrast silk T-shirt could look sensational.

Gloves Will add a stylish touch if they are ladylike silk.

Tights Keep them plain and sheer.

Shoes They must be elegant and comfortable. Never wear new shoes for an occasion where you may be standing for much of the day.

Dinner Dance

Hat Not necessary, though hair bows or ornaments always help to finish off an outfit.

Hair Now's the moment to wear a more elaborate hairstyle. Sweep long hair up or add fullness to short hair. Make use of mousse!

Make-up Intensify the colours slightly more than usual since artificial light tends to drain colour from the face and candlelight can make you look positively ghoulish.

Jewellery Gold or silver always look classy but sparkling costume jewellery or crystal will catch the light and, worn as a necklace or earrings, draw attention to your face.

Outfit The little black dress may well come into its own worn with some fabulous jewellery, but gold, silver and all the jewel colours look stunning in luxury fabrics such as silk taffeta, velvet or brocade.

Gloves Unless you are trying to emulate a 'fifties' Audrey Hepburn look, forget them.

Tights or stockings Should be sheer, dark, seamed and sexy!

Shoes The best you can afford, since when you dance your feet will be noticed. Use shoe bows to enhance a plain pair.

School Speech/Sports Day

Hat Not necessary unless it's an integral part of your character and your child is used to seeing you in one.

Hair Keep your regular hairstyle or your child is bound to make a loud remark about it to everyone in earshot!

Make-up Keep it light and natural.

Jewellery Keep it minimal and understated.

Outfit Aim for smart layers of separates which can take you inside and outdoors. A coordinating jacket, blouse and skirt would be ideal.

Gloves Leather gloves would be fine for cold weather and, in a bright colour, would be an informal fashion accessory.

Tights Opaque coloured tights which tone with your outfit if it's cold or flesh-coloured tights if it's warm.

Shoes Imagine a school playing field or a slippery parquet floor and don't choose stilettos! Stylish but sensible are the buzz words.

Firework Party

Hat Keep your ears warm with anything except a knitted tea cosy! Casual hats mean berets, beanies or the flattering cowl/hood styles.

Hair Keep hairstyle simple and casual. Hair flattened by hats can be revitalized by bending your head and brushing forward from the roots to the tips.

Make-up Keep it natural or make it fun by painting on elaborate silver or gold eye make-up in the shape of stars and moons.

Jewellery Fun jewellery such as chunky bracelets or unusual earrings will pep up casual clothes.

Outfit Don't wear boring old jeans! Add your own glow and crackle with a long sweater and leggings or casual trousers and a silk blouse topped with a flying jacket. Trousers make sense in the cold. Mix the old with the new, the rough textures with the smooth and make your own individual clothes cocktail.

Gloves and scarves In brightly-coloured wool for warm weatherproofing.

Tights Warm and patterned or socks under trousers.

Shoes Flat loafers or lace-ups make sense for outdoors but take a pair of flat pumps to change into once the party moves indoors.

The best way to lose fat, and keep it off, is to combine healthy eating with regular exercise. Exercise raises the metabolic rate, making the body use food energy for fuel, so there is less surplus to be stored as fat. Exercise hard for half an hour, three times a week, and the post-workout burn-off can make a difference of 5–10 lb (2–4.5 kg) over a year, with no special diet. Your figure will look good, too. All that excess flab, toned up, will make you look trimmer and slimmer. Don't be discouraged if your scales don't show a dramatic weight loss – muscle weighs heavier than fat. The important thing is that your improved body shape will be a just reward for your efforts.

The idea of exercise often makes the uninitiated squirm. If you haven't attempted any regular exercise since your schooldays, all sorts of excuses abound: exercise is boring (you haven't yet found an activity that you enjoy); exercise doesn't do you any good (fantasies of a chairbound culture); I haven't got time (give up watching television); my job keeps me fit (being on your feet all day doesn't mean you are fit). Have you heard them before? Well, now's the time to do something positive and put your whole body in harmony with your appearance.

The secret of making the first move is to find a sporting activity or an exercise class, or both, which you will enjoy. Once the beauty benefits (glowing skin, bright eyes and fresh complexion, thanks to improved circulation) begin to register, nobody interested in their health and wellbeing could ignore the far-reaching consequences of feeling fitter.

Bodily Benefits

The penalties of physical idleness range from obesity, diabetes, arthritis, heart disease, hypertension, osteoporosis and constipation. It's never too late to start improving your health and provided you begin gently, checking with your doctor for further advice, you can begin to benefit from the results. Exercising regularly helps to keep the circulatory system in good working order, which in turn reduces the likelihood of coronary heart disease and also keeps blood pressure down. Coupled with a sensible diet, exercise will help you burn up calories and gain muscle, resulting in a more streamlined appearance. It will also delay the deterioration in strength, stamina and suppleness which accompanies the ageing process and, best of all, exercise can alleviate stress.

Heavenly Benefits

Stress is the scourge of modern society, the physical and mental tell-tale signs are increasingly common in a workaholic environment; interrupted sleep, feelings of exhaustion, chest pains, migraine, skin rashes, lethargy, abnormal eating, drinking or smoking, becoming accident-prone, being overly aggressive, and frustrated at making more effort yet achieving less.

Learning to relax through some form of exercise can help, since it is not the external situation in itself which produces stress, but our reaction to it. People under pressure improve psychologically from a spot of quiet meditation, which teaches detachment and emotional control. When it is combined with a physical outlet, the old adage that a well-tuned body means a well-tuned mind can be seen to be true.

Recent research indicates that the feeling of positive wellbeing which follows exercise may be due to a series of complex chemical changes stemming from the brain which help to release energy and tension. In other words, exercise is good for you! But here's the crunch. It's got to be the right exercise performed in the right frame of mind, or you'll never know the pleasure or the benefits that can be gained from regular activity.

Making the Right Moves

Anyone who regards exercise as a chore hasn't yet discovered the right route to fitness. Fundamental reasons for starting a more active lifestyle vary from wanting to get out of a social rut to having a real desire to improve overall health. However, it's no use trying to fit in too much at once, or setting yourself impossible targets, or travelling a long way, when you know it will only add pressure to your current workload. On the other hand, you must make an effort, otherwise you'll achieve nothing. As with everything, a balanced, rather than obsessional, approach is the answer.

Ask yourself whether you want instruction. company or competition from your chosen exercise. Are you a team person or a solitary one? If you lack self-discipline, being part of a team will keep you on the right track. Do you want an activity which could involve organization, like booking a tennis court in advance, or do you prefer spontaneous exercise such as running, where, if you are short of time, you need rely on nobody but yourself? If you join a club, how much are you prepared to spend? Swimming, for instance, is likely to be cheaper than squash. On the other hand, clubs may score highly on the social scale. Maybe you don't want your exercise to be purely recreational. Self-defence, for example, fulfils a functional purpose and yoga can teach us about self-awareness as well as body-awareness.

Whatever your choice of exercise, it will always prove to be a source of inspiration because the impetus will come from you. It's your way of expressing yourself through movement, and a positive approach to exercise means it can be tailor-made to your requirements, leaving you free to enjoy the extra vitality it creates.

Fitness at Home

There may be reasons why it's more convenient to exercise at home, in which case all you have to do is to set aside some time for yourself and exercise some discipline! Even if you don't fancy a full-frontal attack on the fat, you can sidle up to the idea slowly!

House Work Out

Sometimes the simplest things can get you going – it might be just a case of utilizing some household equipment or playing with your children, but it could spur you on to greater things!

● Who needs children to have an excuse to play? The humble hula hoop is a marvellous waist whittler and can be whirled around in a spare moment – or you could skip with an ordinary skipping rope. You'll need trainers to protect you against the jarring on the knees and ankles and a sports bra for breast comfort, but you will soon get into a practised rhythm.

● If you do have children, join in the fun and make playtime an exercise in fitness, too. Play their jumping games and join in with music and movement.

● Make use of the stairs in your house. Walk up and down them as briskly and as often as possible to strengthen your thighs, calves and ankles.

● Make light work of household chores and turn them to your advantage. Whether you are making the beds or vacuuming the carpets, exaggerate your movements so that you stretch your body gracefully.

● When you are doing the washing-up, practise some leg-lifts. Raise your leg slowly behind and to the side.

● Strengthen your stomach muscles while sitting in front of the television. Practise pulling in your stomach and then relaxing. You can do the same thing with your buttocks, tightening and releasing them to firm your bottom.

● Make use of kitchen cans. Take two unopened cans of baked beans (or something similar) and use them like weights while you are waiting for the kettle to boil. To strengthen your arms, push them upwards, then outwards from the shoulders. Then bring them together in front of the bust and you'll also improve upper arm flab and strengthen your chest muscles.

Firm Resolutions

When you feel ready to progress, you may like to clear a space in your bedroom and consider some more specific exercises. If you haven't done any exercise lately, remember:

● It's never too late to start.

● Always check with your doctor if in doubt about your health.

● Begin slowly and steadily, adding to the number of repeat exercises as you improve and become more supple.

● Every session should start with a warm-up to help raise body temperature and lessen the chance of injuries.

● Always exercise in a warm airy room, as cold muscles are injury-prone.

● Never strain when exercising. Don't stress the joints with excessive bouncing. Do what you can, when you can, but build up slowly at all times.

● Don't exercise after a heavy meal. Wait at least two hours.

● Use an exercise mat – your bones will thank you!

● Combine specific exercises with a more general fitness programme which may include swimming or running to help strengthen heart and lungs.

● If you are following a specific exercise routine, pay attention to your body alignment. Backs and knees should always be protected from strain.

● Exercising in front of a full-length mirror makes it easier to check and correct your position if necessary.

● Always finish with a period of relaxation to allow the body to cool down.

● Always wear something comfortable, such as a leotard or tracksuit.

● Breathe steadily during all exercises.

● Try exercising to music if it helps to build a natural rhythm into your routine.

Trim Tactics

1. Warm-up stretch Stand with your feet comfortably apart, hands by your sides. Bend your knees and let your arms come down to touch the floor. Sweep your arms up slowly and straighten your knees. Swing your arms up above your head and reach up with your whole body, keeping your heels on the floor. Stretch right up on tiptoe and bring your arms around in a circular movement to your sides. Repeat five times.

2. Head roll Relieve neck tension by dropping your head forward so that your chin almost touches your chest. Slowly roll your head across to the left and back to the starting position. Now roll it to the right and back to the starting position. Finally, rotate the whole head in a clockwise movement and then anti-clockwise. Repeat the whole exercise three times.

3. Chin stretch Cheat a double chin and stretch your head backwards, keeping your bottom lip over your top lip. Hold for a few moments and then relax. For a second exercise and light relief, try reaching your nose with the tip of your tongue.

4. Shoulder circles Raise your shoulders as high as possible, rotating them backwards in a circular action. Repeat five times and then rotate six times in the opposite direction. Good for releasing tension, too.

5. Arm shapers Tighten arm flab by pushing your arms forward as far as possible, with your fingers pointing upwards. Return to your chest. Repeat five times.

6. Bust firmer Aim for a fluid movement. Begin with your arms at the sides, legs slightly apart. Stretch your arms out fully, then bring them together in a crossover motion in front of your thighs. Then swing your arms wide and bring them together in a crossover at waist level. Aim to do six crossovers from start position until your arms are above your head. Then return to thigh level in the same manner, swinging your arms out and crossing them in. Repeat this whole sequence once more.

7. Waist whittler Stand with your feet apart, knees bent slightly. With your hands behind your head, bend to the right as far as you can comfortably go. Repeat five times each side, keeping your body straight.

8. Back strengthener Kneel on all fours, palms flat, arms straight. Suck in your tummy and arch your back. Relax slowly.

9. Tummy toner Lie on the floor with your knees bent, legs together and feet flat. Curl your shoulders slowly off the floor, pulling in your stomach, keeping your chin tucked into your chest and your feet firmly on the floor. Slide your hands along your thighs to your knees for support and hold to a count of five. Curl back down slowly. Repeat once more.

10. Hips Lie on the floor and roll on to your left side. Breathe in and swing your right leg forwards and then back. Breathe out. Repeat five times, then roll on to your right side for the same movements.

11. Thigh trimmer Stand with your hands behind your head, feet slightly apart. Step back with the left leg, holding it straight, and lower your body by bending your right knee at right angles. Hold for a count of five, then push forward with your left leg to return to start position. Repeat, stepping back with your right leg. Do the complete movement five times for each leg.

Head roll

Chin stretch

Shoulder circles

Arm shapers

Bust firmer

Waist whittler

Back strengthener

Tummy toner

Thigh trimmer

Bottom booster

Ankle trim

12. Bottom booster Lie face down, arms at the sides. Raise your left leg, not too high, and hold for a count of five. Slowly lower and then raise and lower the right leg. Do the complete sequence once more.

13. Ankle trim Sit on the floor, leaning back on bent forearms. Bend your left leg and cross your right leg over it. Use the right foot to trace imaginary circles in the air, first one way, then the other, five times. Change over legs and repeat.

14. Relax Sit on the floor with your body straight. Raise your arms and bend forward, letting your arms relax at the sides of your feet. Relax your whole body and rest for a while.

Beating the Age Barrier

You are as young as you feel. Think positively about your attitudes and don't worry about your age. You are never too old to change your appearance, pursue new interests or be vital and attractive. After all, age is a concept of comparisons; an athlete may be over the hill by her mid-twenties, but a fifty-year-old politician is considered young and potentially dynamic. The quest for eternal youth goes hand in hand with making the most of what you have. A little effort pays off, for when you look good, you feel good and your spirits are high.

Fitness Formula for Body and Mind

1. Take pride in your appearance and your confidence will soar.

2. Develop your own style to suit your colouring, figure type and way of life, but don't try to compete with the young.

3. Experiment with new cosmetics and hairstyles and regularly review and update your wardrobe.

4. Keep some time for yourself every day and use it to do or learn something that interests you. Remember that physical and mental inactivity accelerates the ageing process.

5. Enjoy a healthy diet which includes plenty of fresh fruit and vegetables for those vitality-giving vitamins.

6. Daily exercise will relax and elevate your mood as well as giving you a fit body and a keen mind.

7. Practise some preventive medicine by giving up smoking, drinking less alcohol, cutting down on salty, sugary and fatty foods and avoiding eye strain, back strain and stressful situations. Your eyes, teeth, gums, back, heart and lungs will all benefit.

8. Get plenty of sleep so that your body has a chance to regenerate and recharge.

9. Learn to relax your mind and body. Deep breathing and massage can help to reduce tension and stress.

10. Don't aim to be a perfectionist when it comes to chores. Tackle what you can, when you can, and leave the rest.

Take it from the Top

Take a long, careful look at yourself to check that you don't look older than you should. Outdated make-up, a hairstyle that no longer suits you or a stooping posture can all add on the years.

● Take your hair in hand. Enhance your natural colour to cover grey hairs. As your skin pales with age, a lighter hair shade looks softer and less artificial.

● Greying hair can become coarse and wiry, so consider a change of style to suit the new texture.

● Long hair worn loose seldom suits older women, so put it up or take advice from your hairdresser about a cut which suits your face shape.

● Wrinkles and lines can't be made to disappear, but a good skin care routine can slow down the ageing process. Skin gets drier with age, so use a moisturizer liberally.

● Reshape your eyebrows so that they don't droop. Tweeze away straggly hairs and pencil in a higher replacement line.

● Don't encourage frown lines by not wearing glasses for close work when you should. Presbyopia (the diminishing ability of the eye to focus) sets in around 40, so visit your optician for an eye test.

● Define your eyes with make-up. Keep it soft and subtle, with no frosty shades if your eyelids are slightly crêpey. If you don't like wearing mascara and you have fair lashes, consider having them dyed.

● Subtle blusher adds warmth and shape to a skin which may have paled with age. Cream blushes are kinder to drier skins.

● Lips should be defined with a pencil outline, lifting the outer corners of the lips minimally above the natural line. Fill in with a matt cream lipstick.

● Chins and necks can be an age giveaway. Beat the sag with exercise. Say eeee, aaaa, oooo, and feel those jaw muscles working. Moisturize well to prevent the skin from becoming crêpey.

● Good posture is vital, so look after your spine and walk tall with energy, shoulders back, tummy tucked in. Keep your vertebrae supple and never slump, however tired you feel.

● Shape up upper arm flab. Utilize the door frame; put your hands level with your head, then push and relax, push and relax, ten times each day.

● Invest in a good bra and keep your bustline firm with exercise. Hold your hands in prayer position, push the palms together hard, and relax. Repeat ten times daily.

● A thickening waistline could be part of the hormonal changes that occur after menopause, but don't let extra pounds accumulate. Watch your diet and cut down on fats and sugars.

● Flatten stomach flab by sitting upright and straight on a chair. Push your stomach out, breathing out, then pull it in very hard, breathing in deeply. Repeat ten times daily.

● Bottoms often bear the brunt of cellulite, those hard-to-shift fatty deposits. Massage and exercise can help. Firm your buttocks when sitting down by first contracting the right buttock, then the left, then both together. Repeat ten times daily.

● Hips and thighs are shapely when firm, not fat. Tone up the muscles while you are sitting down. Keep your feet and knees tightly together. Contract your muscles while pressing your knees together as if you were holding a piece of paper between them and your inner thighs. Hold the contraction for a count of six. Release and repeat five times daily.

● Keep your hands from ageing fast by wearing protective gloves for household chores and using hand cream to moisturize the skin.

● Walk barefoot with your toes spread wide to strengthen your feet. Use flat shoes to walk for exercise. It's the easiest and cheapest way to get around.

A Fitting Finale

Looking good and feeling good – the two are synonymous with stylish looks that can be adapted from today's fashions and worn with confidence. Discovering the person you are can alter your expectations of life and broaden your interests and experience. Taking your image in hand and developing a new healthy lifestyle and beauty routine will be both rewarding and enjoyable. Finding your own style will change your life!

INDEX

Note: Numbers in italics refer to illustrations, diagrams or tables.